IoTtransform

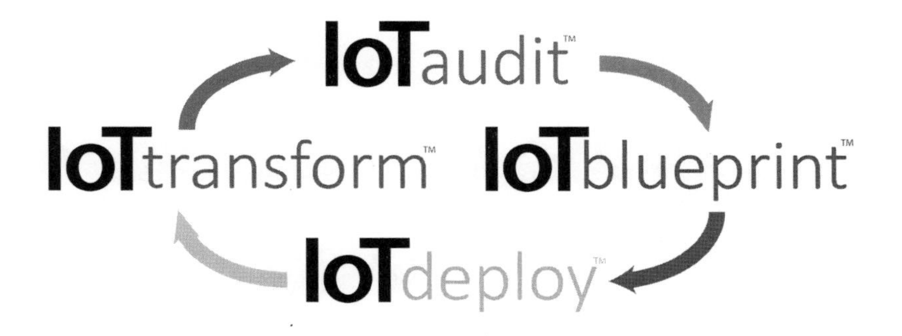

The System that Drives Successful Business Transformation using the Internet of Things

Steve Grady
President and CEO Enviro-Controls

IoTtransform - The System that Drives Successful Business Transformation using the Internet of Things
By Steve Grady

ISBN 978-0-9982649-0-5
Library of Congress control number

Printed in the United States of America.
Publisher: Verixis LLC, 12800 Whitewater Dr. Suite 100, Minnetonka,MN. 55343

Verixis books may be purchased for educational, business or sales promotional use. Online editions are also available for most titles (http://www.verixis.com/books). For more information contact our corporate & institutional sales department: 952-222-7925 or contact@verixis.com.
Revision History for the First Edition
2016-10-15: First Release

Acknowledgments

Wow - writing a book is herculean task! My new heartfelt admiration for all authors who have taken on this task, and especially those who have informed and shaped my thinking.

Many thanks to my fantastic family who put up with me being hidden away in my man cave office at all times of the day and night trying to figure out the best way to explain and present the IoT Business Transformation System.

Thank you to my many business associates over the last 3 decades who have been an integral part of my learning journey. I am a composite of our discussions and your support.

Special thanks to my IoTaudit co-creator, IoT advisor, and good friend Blair Wilson.

Contents

What to Expect

Defining the Future While Herding Cats...

How to Create your IoT Success

Welcome - It is great to have you here! I look forward to helping you realize a successful Internet of Things deployment resulting in a high return IoT Business Transformation.

When working with our clients we have found that one of the biggest issues affecting Internet of Things Business Transformations is the very nature of the IoT deployment project itself. IoT projects are very complex as they cut across many groups in a company, utilize new technologies, include external partners, and results only come from changing how you do business. On the upside, there can be significant business gains through intelligent use of Internet of Things capabilities. Many companies have profited from M2M, SCADA and Remote Monitoring solutions over the last 25 years. The emergence of new IoT sensors, hardware, mobile connectivity, security protocols, low power high performance computing, hand-held apps, and software platforms will now enable hundreds of thousands of companies to realize profitable IoT-driven business transformations.

This book was designed to help you create a successful IoT deployment by using the IoT Business Transformation System. There is no panacea or short cut to a successful IoT deployment given the technical complexity, logistics and number of people who get involved in your IoT project. But if you embrace the proven IoT Business Transformation System methodologies, techniques and tools explained in this book you will be significantly ahead of your competition.

Who will benefit from IoTtransform?

There are 4 types of organizations who will profit from successful IoT business transformation:

1. **IoT End-Users** - Companies, Cities, Universities and Organizations who integrate the Internet of Things into their current infrastructure to create business transformation.
2. **Managed Services Providers** – Information Technology MSPs are End-User partners for outsourced computing and networking infrastructure, software, cloud services and network administration. IT MSPs understand their customers' IT infrastructure and can provide value-added IoT capabilities that drive business transformation
3. **Control System Integrators** – CSIs are End-User partners for outsourced Operational Technology system integration, hardware, software, equipment installation, operation, and maintenance. CSIs have skills in electrical, safety and security installations which are well suited for IoT deployments.
4. **Smart Connected Product Vendors** – SCPs are often original equipment manufacturers (OEMs) who are now integrating sensing, intelligence and network connectivity into their products. These solutions are enabling IoT solutions areas such as Smart Cities, Smart Energy, Smart Factory and Smart Transportation.

What Are Your Challenges?

Many of the aspects of an IoT deployment will be new to your organization. Addressing the intersection of processes, customers, markets, hardware, software, networking, security, data analysis, information technology, operations technology, and organizational culture is incredibly difficult. You have business pain point challenges you are looking resolve using IoT, but It is hard to know exactly where to start and how to identify the path to success. This book has been written specifically to help you surmount these challenges.

We Have Been In Your Shoes

The team at Enviro-Controls had exactly the same challenges you face when we decided to create the IoT Smart Overlay Platform as a Service. We used the all tools in this book to: identify our IoT Target Outcome, create our Strategy, document our TASKs plan, blueprint, deploy, and transform our company using IoT.

What Are Your Choices?

In the absence of not having the IoT Business Transformation System, you will be left to use your traditional business planning, project management, change management and product launch tools and processes. If you are like many organizations, your tool sets have created marginal results. Don't feel alone, many business transformation projects fail for various reasons as will be discussed (and solved) in later chapters.

What do I Need to be Successful?

You will need to utilize a proven structured process that provides a coherent coordinated approach across your policies, guidelines and actions that creates an IoT solution that will overcome your key business challenge.

How Does This Book Help?

This book provides the frameworks, planning systems, tools and techniques to help drive IoT Business Transformation success. Internet of Things business transformation is one of the most complex projects an organization might pursue. IoTtransform provides the system for success.

How Do I Find IoT Business Transformation Support?

As with all "How-To" books you and your organization may need additional help to accomplish your IoT business transformation objectives. The Resources chapter at the end of this book will introduce you to organizations that can assist you during your IoT journey.

The 3 Key IoT Planning and Execution Systems used in this Book

There are 3 main systems and tool suites we will use to create your Internet of Things Success.

#1 – IoT Business Transformation System (IoT BTS for short)

The IoT BTS will be explained in great detail in subsequent chapters, but here are the high level summaries of the 4 components:

IoTaudit - This planning and readiness structured methodology is the essential first step. IoTaudit starts with your Key Business Pain Points that drive the creation of your IoT Target Outcome, and calculates the financial value of solving these pains as described in your IoT Target Outcome. You will create your IoT Strategy and Tasks Plan to guide you toward solving your Business Pain Points. You will also examine your company's Culture to determine how that will dictate your company's ability to use IoT to transform your business.

IoTblueprint - In this phase, you will architect your IoT network and identify all the components that need to be procured including sensors, gateways, network connections, IoT software services, cloud storage, business software applications, and managed services .

IoTdeploy - Now you will install, provision, test, and scale your IoT network using best-in-class product and services. We will explore several options for deploying your network that significantly reduces risk.

IoTtransform - This phase is the most important of all as you use your new IoT Data to achieve your IoT Target Outcome. It is important to note, that many of your company's staff who will be intimately involved in this 4th IoT Business Transformation System phase were not involved in the first 3 phases of your IoT project. This needs to be actively addressed as we will discuss in the IoTtransform chapter.

#2 – The BEST System

The BEST System is a universal problem solving methodology and is the fundamental underpinnings of the IoT Business Transformation System. There are 5 parts to the BEST System: Target Outcome and BEST stands for the Baseline, Expectations, Strategy and Tasks processes. This will be covered in detail in the BEST System chapter, but as an introduction:

IoT Target Outcome – This statement describes your IoT business transformation success. The format is succinct: "We will Improve the Target Area from the Current Value to a Target Value by the Target Date achieving a Target Financial Return"

Baseline – identify your current status in all the areas relevant to the Current Value of your Target Area. Then Backtrack from your Target Value to your Current Value identifying all the steps using "5 Whys".

Expectations - identify and discuss all your IoT stakeholder expectations. Assumed and missed expectations doom IoT projects.

Strategy – using your Baseline and Backtrack analysis you build the StratGraph that goes from your Current Value to your Target Value.

TASKs Plan – Identify all the tasks that need to be accomplished to realize your IoT Target Outcome. TASK stands for: Time, Accountability, Steps, and Keep score.

#3 – Organizational Culture Assessment Instrument – OCAI

One of the fundamental drivers of your IoT business transformation success will be your ability to create change in your organization. In order to drive these IoT-related changes, you must understand the impact of IoT on your organizational culture. The OCAI survey is a powerful but easy to use tool to assess and document your organizational culture. With your culture understood, you can map your IoT project to your against your culture to determine the synergies and roadblocks.

This Book Will Point You Toward Success

This is not a huge book as I wanted to optimize the information delivery in a clear and succinct manner. I don't know about you, but I have a hard time getting through hundreds of pages trying to extract the key learnings. Once you have read through this book, you should have an excellent understanding of the IoT systems, processes and tools you need to drive a successful Internet of Things business transformation.

Emphasizing Risk Management

A key common thread through this entire book is Risk Management. I have found over my decades of managing product development and Go-To-Market projects that you always need to focus on managing your risks. As Intel's Andy Grove aptly put: "Only the Paranoid Survive." I agree, it is vital to make sure you have a solid plan, prepare for contingencies ahead of time, and always manage your project with a 360 degree view.

Creating a Positive Outlook

Risk Management is vital, but what will get your IoT Business Case approved, planning documents embraced, IoT network deployed and your Business Transformed is a positive outlook that you and your team will succeed. As Andy Groves' partner at Intel Robert Noyce said "Optimism is an essential ingredient of innovation. How else can the individual welcome change over security, adventure over staying in safe places?"

Deploying an Internet of Things-based Business Transformation will move many people in your organization from their "safe place". It will impact your company's culture and that is why we assess your organizational culture right after the IoTaudit. As the leader of your IoT Project, you will need to have a spirit of unwavering high energy approach that will inspire all your IoT stakeholders with your vision of success.

This book is written with strong positive outlook as we have seen many significant successful IoT-based business transformations. IoT has been implemented by many organizations around the world and you can do it too. Using the IoT Business Transformation System will be the key driver in your IoT success.

So let's get going!

Why Internet of Things for Business Transformation?

Giving Your Infrastructure a Voice...

The Business Drivers for the Internet of Things

We are going to leverage the Internet of Things to enable your business success. But how can we cut through the hype and understand how IoT can address your key business challenges? The IoT Business Transformation System is a framework-based tool suite designed to identify your key IoT business drivers, help you avoid expensive mistakes and create your optimal IoT solution. You will leverage the process that other companies have used in their IoT deployments that are generating measurable benefits. Our shared goal is to use the systems and tools in this book to create the optimal IoT solution for your business.

Finding Your Right Way to Utilize IoT

IoT is a big deal. It has become a dominant technology and business trend, following the major shifts to mobility and cloud computing that shaped the last decade in technology. The numbers are indeed staggering. IDC forecasts the number of connected devices which exclude PCs, smart phones and tablets, will reach over 28 billion in 2020 from the current 9 billion devices in 2013. These numbers are 10x the 3 billion connected PCs, tablets, and handsets today. The Internet of things will impact many industries, creating new winners and losers based on a company's ability to adapt to a world where things are connected.

Companies are deploying IoT solutions that drive benefits in enhanced customer service, increased revenue, improved supply chain and use of assets. IoT also is being used to improve sustainability efforts in the areas of energy, water and natural resources.

IoT is not new - as sensors and remote monitoring networks have been used for 30 years. But the emergence of new technologies: inexpensive sensors, ubiquitous wireless, cloud computing and Big Data are driving new business models with high ROI.

Internet of Things – A Gigantic Economic Tide

Economic impact of Internet of Everything is forecasted by Cisco to grow by $19 trillion between 2014 and 2020. This 6-year growth exceeds the entire US 2013 economy of $16.5 trillion. IDC estimates there are already 9 billion sensors autonomously generating data, and in 2012 alone the "pull through" market value was almost $5 trillion.

IDC also estimates that by 2020, the total value of the industry will have reached around $9 trillion. That value isn't just the cost of hardware. It includes everything from connectivity, systems, data analytics and security. For example, your Internet-enabled thermostat will need a network connection, the systems and User Interface service that allows you to access it, and security that prevents a thermostat hack.

The same IDC survey found that half of CTOs and CIOs have never had a conversation with their suppliers about potential savings—or possible disruptions—that IoT services might cause for their business.

Accenture conducted a worldwide survey of more than 1,400 business decision makers and found that 84% think their organization would potentially benefit from IIoT in multiple ways. But a mere 7% said they have actually created a comprehensive IIoT strategy and invested appropriate funds to support that strategy.

So is it surprising that the Internet of Things has become such a slippery concept and subject to so much hype?

Leveraging IoT for Your Organization

Internet of Things sensors are essentially a way to give a voice to "Infrastructure Data" that is has been inaccessible. This IoT Sensor data is analyzed with other existing data sources to provide new "Operational Intelligence" to solve business problems. Large IoT deployments will create "Big Data" datasets that are too large for traditional data processing systems and require new processing technologies. Developing the ability to extract useful knowledge from IoT data needs to be considered a key corporate strategic asset that drives business performance optimization.

Addressing the Frustrations with IoT

The Internet of Things is a complex and an "all-things-to-all-people" concept. Many of our client discussions has surrounded the following:

- So much hype – what is real, what is true?
- So many wild prognostications and forecasts.
- So many new technologies, protocols and architectures
- So many vendors doing only a piece of an IoT solution.
- So many integration and deployment hurdles.
- Unclear return on investment economics.
- Many companies struggle with the introduction of IoT that requires changes in processes, new equipment, new data analysis, new skills and new attitudes.
- What processes and tools do I use to make good decisions?

"I-o-what?" an Alphabet Soup of Acronyms...

Before we get started let's clear up some of the various terms used in IoT discussions:

IoT – Internet of Things is the interconnection of uniquely identifiable embedded computing devices connected with an Internet infrastructure.

IIoT – Industrial IoT – describes a robust IoT implementation for demanding environments in factories, refineries, etc.

IoP – Internet of People – Connecting personal data to the Internet for health, safety, convenience and well-being.

IoE – Internet of Everything. This combines people, things, data and process to turn information into intelligent actions. Essentially IoT + IoP.

M2M – Machine to Machine technologies allow both wireless and wired systems to communicate with other devices for monitoring, control and telematics functions. M2M is now combined into IoT.

SCADA – Sensory Control And Data Acquisition is a term that has been used for several decades to describe remote monitoring and control of diverse and disperse devices. These functions are embodied in IoT architectures and applications.

Internet of Things Benefits

The evolution of IoT technology has introduced opportunities for business in many industries. For organizations who are already using IOT technology, the effect on their business has been dramatic improvements in efficiency, significant capital expenditure savings, and operational expenditure savings.

Infonetics conducted a study in 2014 with 163 companies concerning M2M and IOT service adoption drivers. The following list was the percent of respondents rating the factor very important or critical:

- Business agility 72%
- Improve the quality of our products or services 70%
- Improve customer satisfaction 68%
- Generate new revenue 65%
- Improve workflow 63%
- Lower cost 61%
- Improve employee satisfaction 57%

Additionally, solutions and services enabled by IOT extended to:

- Customer loyalty
- Improved product functionality
- Automated information exchanges
- New product innovation
- New revenue streams

There are many industries who can benefit from the transformative ability of the Internet of things. A few applications include:

- Asset monitoring
- Climate control
- Education
- Energy management
- Healthcare
- IT networks
- Regulatory and compliance
- Retail
- Safety

- Smart cities
- Smart lighting
- Surveillance and security
- Tank monitoring
- Transportation

Vodafone recently released the 2016 edition of their M2M Adoption Barometer. You can find this research report on www.enviro-controls.com/iottransform. What's interesting are the statistics from their 2013 barometer when they interviewed 327 qualified respondents. At that point in time, 12% of the respondents had already launched an M2M project, 55% said M2M was a key priority, and 36% saw significant return from M2M deployments. Fast-forward to 2016, when 1096 qualified respondents indicated the following; 89% of the respondents have increased their use of IoT in the past 12 months, 63% have achieved significant ROI, 24% of IT budgets are now spent on the IoT, and 48% use IoT to support large-scale business transformations.

The qualified Vodafone respondents were spread across the world in 17 countries from every industry type, both small and medium businesses, and large multinationals. The overall IT budgets in these companies ranged from $15,000 to more than $75 million.

IoT is a bigger priority than ever as 76% of all the companies Vodafone interviewed said that IoT will be critical for the future success of any organization in their sector. Why IoT is so important to your business future is the ever-increasing pressure to get results. At this point in time, IoT technologies have emerged as the leading category in IT spend essentially tied with clouded hosting initiatives, data analytics, and mobility applications.

Most importantly, many respondents are seeing significant return on investment for IOT, with another large portion of the respondents seeing some ROI. One of the most telling results is to look at how a company's revenue has changed through the use of Internet of Things. The survey respondents were asked how has their company revenue changed in the past year and the respondents were divided into two categories: adopters reporting significant ROI, and adopters reporting some/little ROI. **For the group of adopters reporting significant ROI, 21% reported revenues increasing by greater than 10%.** You can see there is a clear correlation between adopting IoT projects with significant ROI and increasing revenues dramatically.

Additional Reasons for Adopting IoT

Harvard Business Review conducted a survey of 269 companies concerning their IoT plans, motivations and results. Initial reasons for adopting IoT:

- 51% - Enhanced Customer Service
- 44% - Increased revenues from Services or Products
- 38% - Improved use of assets in the field
- 35% - Acquiring more information for big data efforts

Respondents used IoT for: Asset tracking, Security, Energy data management, Field Force Management, Condition-based monitoring, and Fleet Management.

IoT Drives Results and Rewards

What these 269 companies found after their IoT implementation:

- 62% found IoT increased customer responsiveness
- 58% say it increased collaboration within the business
- 54% credit IoT with increasing market insights
- 54% believe it increased employee productivity

Many respondents said that IoT had enabled them to change their organization's core strategy. New business models were created by offering new services.

Who Impacts IoT Deployment Success?

The HBR survey as identified the top 3 influencers that impact IoT deployment success are:

- 59% Senior Management
- 51% Business Units/Operations Management
- 44% from IT Management

The Senior Leaders across all organizations must understand IoT fundamentals and the strategic importance of IoT in their Business Plans. Business Units often are responsible for the Operations Technology and infrastructure that is the heart of many businesses. IT organizations are looking to enable their business units by combining new IoT data with current enterprise data and perform Big Data analysis to provide new insights and business optimization.

Data Driven Decision Making Drives Productivity Gains

Companies that use Data Driven Decision making (e.g. Big Data analysis) have demonstrated conclusively to increase company productivity 4%-6%. Data Driven Decision-making is also correlated with higher:

- Return on Assets
- Return on Equity
- Asset Utilization
- Market Value

Another study suggested that companies with higher utilization of Big Data technologies is associated with 1%-3% higher productivity than average firms.

IoT and Big Data are Intrinsically Linked

Internet of Things deployments create data that is used for both short term infrastructure management and longer term data analysis. IoT data will be combined into a company's overall data analytics strategy which is a key part of today's corporate strategy:

- 88% of companies interviewed say that Big Data analytics are in their company's top three priorities.
- 73% of companies are already investing more than 20 percent of their overall technology budget on Big Data analytics—and more than two in 10 are investing more than 30 percent.
- 53% say that it is now a board level initiative.
- 84% of those surveyed indicated that the use of Big Data analytics "has the power to shift the competitive landscape for my industry" within just the next year.

IoT Initiatives Can Generate Concerns

However, the 269 companies that realized all the IoT benefits also had important concerns:

- 46% Ensuring Privacy and Regulatory Compliance
- 39% Acquiring the needed skills to leverage IoT data
- 35% Managing the growing volumes of data
- 28% Securing IoT Sensors and their data

So IoT pros and cons need to be identified, quantified and balanced to determine the Return on Investment vs. the cost impact of various risks. Let's do a deeper dive and explore the Internet of Things from the perspectives of new applications and new technologies.

Sim ple IoT Concept Diagram

The following diagram from Hanson Inc. is a simple way to look at the relationships of the IoT Sensors Layer and the IoT Data Layer.

At the top of the Diagram are examples of 3 major types of sensors that create Infrastructure Data:

- Sensors that connect to the body for health and safety
- Sensors that connect to other objects with operation, efficiency or progress status
- Sensors that monitor the environment

Infrastructure Sensor Data

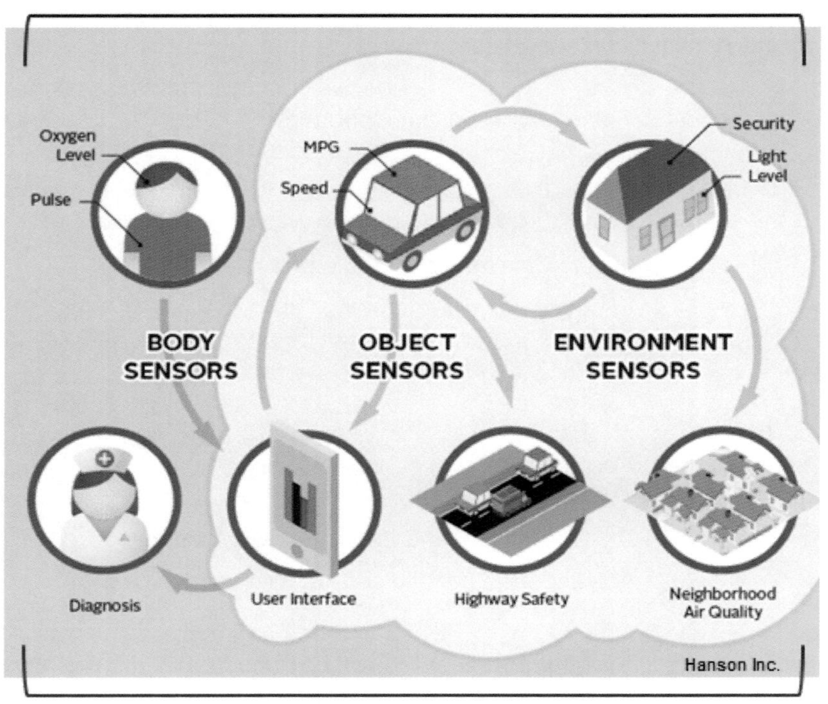

Operational Intelligence

Infrastructure Data is turned into Operational Intelligence through:

- Data Collection
- Data Analysis
- Diagnosis and Actions

This simple structure is the foundation for more complex IoT architectures.

Find Your Application (or be inspired for new ones)

To understand the wide range of IoT applications, quickly scan this list of 77 different IoT applications courtesy of Monnit who supplies a very broad range of IoT sensing devices - www.monnit.com. You will probably find your application here, but this extensive list may give you ideas of other ways to use the Internet of Things in your situation.

1. Access Monitoring
2. Agricultural Monitoring
3. Animal Tracking and Monitoring
4. Apartment Property Management
5. Art Gallery Light and Temperature Monitoring
6. Bank Owned Property Monitoring
7. Bed Bug Extermination Temperature Monitoring
8. Beverage Cooler Temperature Monitoring
9. Boat Bilge Pump Monitoring
10. Boiler Temperature Monitoring
11. Cold Chain Monitoring
12. Cold Weather Protection
13. College Dormitory Monitoring
14. Commercial Plumbing Monitoring
15. Commercial Property Management and Monitoring
16. Commercial Refrigeration Monitoring
17. Construction Equipment Monitoring
18. Convenience Store Management
19. Crawl Space Monitoring
20. Dairy Cooler Temperature Monitoring
21. Data Center Temperature Monitoring

22. Deli Food Cooler Temperature Monitoring
23. Environmental Monitoring Solutions for Floor Maintenance
24. Facility Monitoring
25. Farm to Fork Monitoring
26. Fleet Management
27. Food Service Temperature Monitoring
28. Foreclosed Property Management
29. Frozen Pipes
30. Greenhouse Monitoring
31. Grocery and Cold Chain Monitoring
32. Heating and Cooling System Monitoring
33. Ice Maker Temperature Monitoring
34. Ice Freezer/Cooler Temperature Monitoring
35. Industrial Pressure Sensors and Monitoring
36. Inventory Tracking
37. K9 Unit Temperature Monitoring
38. Laboratory Monitoring
39. Life Cycle Monitoring
40. M2M – Machine to Machine Solutions
41. Medical Refrigerator Temperature Monitoring
42. Morgue Temperature Monitoring
43. Mortuary Cooler Temperature Monitoring
44. Museum Light Exposure Monitoring
45. Organ and Tissue Transplant Cooler Monitoring
46. Parking Garage Monitoring
47. Pet Kennel Temperature Monitoring
48. Pharmaceutical Refrigeration Temperature Monitoring
49. Production Line Monitoring
50. Remote Monitoring For Business
51. Remote Property Monitoring
52. Remote Second Home Monitoring
53. Remote Temperature Monitoring

54. Rental Tool and Equipment Tracking
55. Resort Boiler and Water Heater Monitoring
56. School Cafeteria Cooler Temperature Monitoring
57. Server Room Temperature Monitoring
58. Service Verification Tracking and Monitoring
59. Smart Power Monitoring
60. Storage Unit Monitoring
61. Street Light Monitoring
62. Structural Monitoring
63. Student Housing Monitoring
64. Sump Pump Monitoring
65. Supermarket Food Temperature Monitoring
66. Temperature Monitoring
67. Toilet Water Leak Notification
68. Traffic Monitoring
69. Vacant Property Monitoring
70. Vacation Home Monitoring
71. Vehicle / Traffic Counting
72. Walk-In Cooler Temperature Monitoring
73. Warehouse Monitoring
74. Wastewater Monitoring
75. Water Heater Monitoring
76. Water Leak Detection
77. Wine Storage Monitoring

Smart Services for IoT

Along with these many end-user applications, product vendors create new service offerings using IoT Data. Smart Services are defined as post-sales product support that is enabled by wirelessly capturing and analyzing real-time performance information. Smart Services are usually delivered by manufacturers or service providers to the owners of operators of the equipment. OEMs deploy these solutions across the board, so that support can be given to the installed bases of assets at various global formats.

A Smart Services business plan is comprised of 5 main elements:

1. Service cost savings
2. Greater cash flow
3. Service-native revenue growth
4. Service-driven product revenue growth
5. Increase in profitability

Smart Services provide 4 areas of New Revenue drivers:

- Service Performance
- Product Performance
- Customer Value
- Competitive Advantage

Launching IoT-based Smart Services for your products/services can result in a significant competitive advantage.

Internet of Things is a Powerful Transformation Tool

We can see that Internet of Things projects are driving successful financial results for companies around the world. IoT is fast becoming a powerful tool for business transformation. In order to harness the power of the Internet of Things for your business, a structured approach must be used. The IoT Business Transformation System was created to address this challenge. Let's now dive into the IoT BTS details.

IoT Business Transformation System

Structure and Systems Drive IoT Success...

The purpose of this book is to help you and your organization successfully transform a challenging area of your business using the Internet of Things. In order to accomplish this, we will utilize the IoT Business Transformation System as the fundamental template you will use to successfully realize your Internet of Things goals. As with all successful projects, you need to use a structured system. The IoT Business Transformation System is built on four primary components as shown in the diagram below.

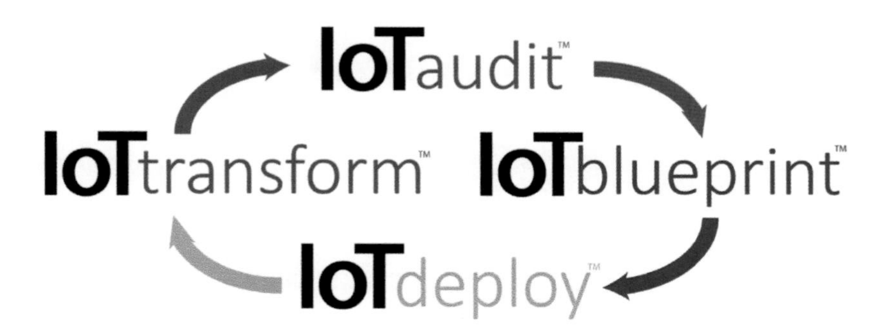

You can see the IoT Business Transformation is a life-cycle model that has interconnected systems. Once you have successfully achieved your IoT Project you will be able to leverage your new IoT deployment and key learnings on your follow-on IoT Projects.

The four components of the IoT Business Transformation System are:

IoTaudit – this tool suite is used to create your IoT Plans that documents your IoT Target Outcome, Baseline all relevant IoT information, identify the Expectations of all the IoT stakeholders involved in your project, produce your IoT Strategy, and create your IoT TASKs Plan.

IoTblueprint – once you have your IoT plans in place, you are now able to architect your IoT deployment. This includes all of the hardware, networks, software platforms, and business applications you will need to implement your IoT network. At this point you will be able to calculate definitive costs for your project and compare these costs to your returns calculated in your IoT audit. This is a key phase gate in your IoT project as you can determine your Return on Investment Go/No Go decision.

IoTdeploy – in this phase you install, test, and scale all your IoT equipment and software: sensors, control devices, gateways, wide area network, IoT services software platform, cloud storage, data analytics, and data visualization software. One of the most important decisions you will make in the IoT deploy phase is who will install, provision, operate, and maintain your network. The IoTaudit results will determine whether your internal organization has the skills and staffing resources required for success. If not, you will need to outsource and partner with other organizations to effectively deploy your IoT network.

IoTtransform – this is "where the rubber meets the road". Your IoT network is just the means to your IoT business transformation end. All of your IoT Team's hard work up until this point has been only to create the data that will be used to realize your IoT Target Outcome. Furthermore, organizational culture plays a very large part in the success or failure of your IoT business transformation. We will conduct an analysis to define your culture and help you facilitate the organizational changes that will be required to achieve a successful IoT outcome.

Underpinning the 4 components of the IoT Business Transformation System are eight key steps that drive the overall process

The 8 Foundations for Successful IoT Business Transformation

1. **IoT Target Outcome** - your IoT success statement and vision document that will be urgently driven by leadership.
2. **Baseline and Backtrack** landscape analysis from your Current Value to your Target Value.

3. **Expectations** interviews and negotiations of all IoT Stakeholders conducted by your IoT Coalition Team.
4. **StratGraph** provides the roadmap for how you will arrive at your IoT success.
5. **TASKs Plan** documents all your IoT tasks with single point of accountabilities and tools to monitor progress.
6. **Blueprint and Deploy** IoT implementation using milestones with short term wins that are celebrated.
7. **Change and Communicate** - drive culture change, deploy new processes, celebrate wins, and reward accountable team members.
8. **Anchor** new Business Transformation processes to become standard habit that achieve IoT Target Outcome success.

Introducing the BEST System

The first five steps of the IoT Business Transformation utilize the BEST System. The BEST System is a simple but powerful methodology that can be used to solve any sort of challenge including your IoT Project.

The first step is your IoT Target Outcome. BEST is an acronym that stands for: Baseline, Expectations, Strategy and TASKs. A chapter is dedicated to each of the component of the BEST System, but here is a quick summary.

IoT Target Outcome – your IoT Target Outcome is your Purpose, it is the "Why" you are doing Internet of Things. It is your IoT vision that everyone involved in your IoT project will be able to understand. Your Target Outcome will be described in a single sentence that takes this structure:

We will improve a Target Area from the Current Value to a Target Value by a Target Date achieving a Target Financial Return.

IoT Target Outcome examples are:

We will improve our factory floor yield from 90% to 95% by December 2017 achieving $800,000 in yearly cost savings.

We will introduce a new data service to our customers starting from no statistics on their product performance to eight new statistics on product performance by June 2017 achieving new revenues of $550,000.

We will meet the regulatory mandate for water quality reducing our current value of 22 ppm to 14 ppm by January 1, 2018 achieving $0 in penalties and no disciplinary actions.

Your IoT Target Outcome must be embraced by your newly formed IoT Coalition team who are responsible for driving the success of your IoT Project. The IoT Coalition will document a vision of what your IoT success looks like, feels like, (and maybe even sounds, smells and tastes like - I love food industry clients!). The more vividly you can describe your IoT Target Outcome, the more your IoT stakeholders will be able to understand and support your IoT success.

Baseline

In order to fully understand where you are today and where you need to be tomorrow for your IoT success, you must baseline your situation. The Baseline process in the IoTaudit will work through all the elements of your IoT project. This includes your current methods for: collecting the IoT data you need from your hardware and software environment, your staff skill sets, who your IoT stakeholders will be, who will become your core IoT Coalition team members, determining your competitive environment, and understand your organizational culture.

In order to effectively create a complete Baseline analysis, an effective tool is to Backtrack from your IoT Target Value backwards to your Current Value. It is difficult to build the path from today to tomorrow using only the perspective of looking into the future. Backtracking is a methodology where you start at your future and work backward to your present. We will talk about Backtracking in detail in the chapter on Baseline.

Expectations

The Expectations process of the BEST System is used to understand all your IoT stakeholder expectations concerning your IoT project. You will discuss, negotiate and document the expectations of your: IoT Coalition team, your immediate management, executive management, and all your people who will be affected by your IoT project. This ranges from your core IoT team members to leadership of other internal organizations to customers and even to competitors.

Expectations is a key process in the BEST System. I think most of us have been involved in projects where other people's expectations were not well understood. The resulting misassumptions either damaged or completely derailed your project. It is vitally important that we identify everyone who will have an impact on your IoT Business Transformation outcome. Spending quality time on the Expectations phase can make or break your IoT project.

Strategy

Famous leaders over many centuries have discussed the concept of strategy. Over several decades of developing corporate and product strategies, I have found that strategy is best articulated and understood as a graph/map. Your IoT Strategy documents your simultaneous paths to your destination. It is how you going to get from your Current Value to your IoT Target Value and includes all of the resources, routes and contingencies that need to be in place as you take this IoT journey. Your IoT Strategy is not absolute. We all know that things change: organizations, economies, competition, and markets are fluid. Therefore, having a StratGraph tool is essential, but it is a living document where the Strategic Action Areas may change over time to meet your IoT Target Outcome.

TASKs

With your IoT Strategy in hand, we breakdown all the individual actions required to realize your IoT Target Outcome and document them in your IoT Implementation TASKs Plan.

In the BEST System TASK is an acronym:

T is for time. Every task has a start date and a finish date to be documented in your project plan. Time is one of the most important measurements of urgency. Urgency is an absolute requirement for IoT business transformation. There is an overall urgency to your project described in your IoT Target Outcome as your Target Date. But obviously, all the tasks that lead up to your Target Date need to be accomplished on time in order to successfully accomplish your Target Outcome.

A is for accountability. Each of your tasks need to have a single person accountable for accomplishing the task. Accountabilities do not reside with groups or teams; they point to a single name. This goes back to the old saying "I'd like to have one hand to shake or one neck to ring". Now accountability in the BEST System is only used in its positive sense. Many organizations use accountability in a negative fashion - that "one neck to ring". Rather in a culture of positive accountability, team members volunteer and own their tasks. Their leadership team gives them the tools and empowerment to be successful. Many studies have shown that a companies with a culture high in positive accountability are often very successful both with their customers and in their financial results.

S is for steps – You will break down your Strategy Map Strategic Actions into atomic subtasks and actions that must be completed in order to realize your IoT Target Outcome. Each step and action will be documented in your IoT Project Planning Tool with specific dependencies, outputs and due dates.

K is for Keep Score – it is vital to know the status and progress of your IoT project at all times. Closely monitoring your progress helps identify urgent issues that need to be addressed. Also, you're able to share successes with your IoT Coalition Team and your IoT stakeholders. The ability to celebrate small wins along the road of your IoT project is a key stimulus to driving the changes in your organization that will create your IoT business transformation.

IoT Business Transformation and PDCA: Plan-Do-Change-Anchor

The 8 Foundations of the IoT Business Transformation System is a modern twist on the classical concept of PDCA which was championed by Edward Demming who credited the inspiration from Walter Shewhart. The four phases:

Plan – The first five foundational steps embodied in the IoTaudit are your IoT Target Outcome and BEST System processes.

Do – The IoTblueprint and IoTdeploy processes implement your IoT network and starts generating your IoT data for alarms, thresholds and analysis. You start to introduce process and cultural change in this step.

Change – The IoTtransform process drives the organizational change required for IoT success. C also stands for Communication, which is vital to a successful IoT business transformation. If your IoT change process is going to take hold, you must over-communicate the value and success of your IoT project to all your IoT stakeholders.

Anchor – In order to cement the changes you're creating from your IoT implementation, they must be anchored into your culture and everyday work life. The IoT-related changes need to become the new norm. As these changes become habit, you'll be able to leverage additional beneficial change on top of this new foundation. More importantly, your next set of IoT change initiatives will be seen by your organization as useful and important. So it is vital to document and communicate your successful results not only in your organization but throughout the entire company, your customers, the financial community.

As we move into the details of the IoT Business Transformation System, remember it is all about achieving your IoT Target Outcome. That is why the name of this book is **IoTtransform**.

The 8 Deadly IoT Mistakes You Must Avoid

Ignore these at your own peril...

The Internet of Things has the potential to significantly improve your organization's financial performance through Business Performance Optimization and/or Market Differentiation. To introduce you to some of the key philosophies, techniques and tools detailed in this book, let's start off our IoT transform journey by identifying the 8 Internet of Things mistakes you must avoid that will cripple your IoT deployment.

#1 – No Clear IoT Target Outcome

There is no doubt that the Internet of Things will transform many businesses, organizations and municipalities over the next decade. Whether you believe the estimate of $19 trillion economic impact from 2014 to 2020, or the more reasonable Gartner Group estimate of $1.9 trillion of IoT value-add, the numbers are staggering. This IoT tidal wave of change is being examined at senior levels of almost every company. It is vitally important that this examination be structured for success. Therefore, the first mistake to avoid is that your organization does not have a clear IoT Target Outcome.

This is most vital step in your IoT Planning, as your IoT Target Outcome is the essential Purpose of your IoT deployment. It is the "Why" you are doing IoT, and will be how you explain your vision to IoT project stakeholders. In this diagram, you can see the importance of your Target Outcome as your Purpose, followed by your Process and then your Product.

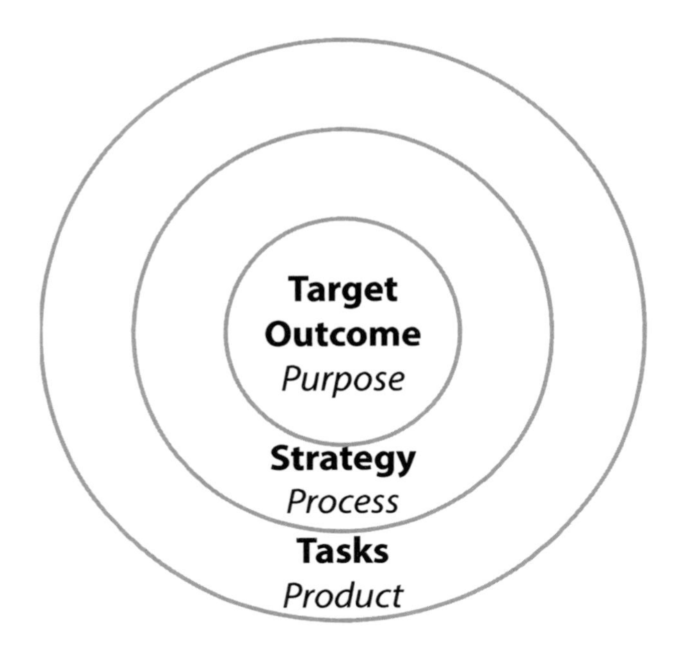

Once you have your IoT Target Outcome defined and documented, your IoT Strategy and Tasks Plan will be much easier to create.

You Must Start with Your Business Pain Points

The Internet of Things is a means to an end. That end is Business Performance Optimization and/or Market Differentiation realized by solving Pain Points in your business. These Pain Points might be areas that are measured closely such as your Key Performance Indicators (KPIs). Or your Pain Points might be new regulations, new infrastructure installation, or new competition. You will have a gap between your Pain Point Current Value and your Target Value. That gap has root causes that potentially can be solved by an IoT implementation.

Your IoT Target Outcome (TO) is not virtual or soft, not a goal, desire or dream. It is a concrete story that you can describe in a detailed Target Outcome Vision document. Writing the TO gives your team a feeling of commitment. The better you can articulate your Target Outcome, the more successful you will be. Your IoT Target Outcome statement takes the form:

"We will improve the Target Area from the Current Value to the Target Value by the Target Date achieving the Target Return."

IoT Target Outcome example statements might be:

We will improve on-time customer shipments from 95% to 99.9% by December 31, 2017 achieving $800,000 in new revenues

We will improve weekly machine uptime to from 90% to 97% by June 1, 2017 achieving $800,000 (maintenance savings/additional revenues)

We will improve incoming parts acceptance from 85% to 99% by October 15, 2017 achieving $350,000 in savings.

The keys to a clear IoT Target Outcome are: Specific target area, current vs. future metric, a specific date to add urgency, and calculate monetary return for your IoT Implementation Business Case ROI.

#2 – Jumping Into IoT Implementation Before Planning

The Internet of Things has a very high cool factor. Each layer of the IoT Reference model represents many advanced technologies.

It is easy to follow the "siren song" of the many IoT hardware and software vendors pushing their products and solutions. Furthermore, there are a lot of IoT maker kits that can be used to demonstrate small scale IoT capabilities. But as we will see in Mistake #8, successful IoT deployments must scale. You must utilize a structured IoT planning methodology to realize a successful IoT Target Outcome.

IoT Reference Model

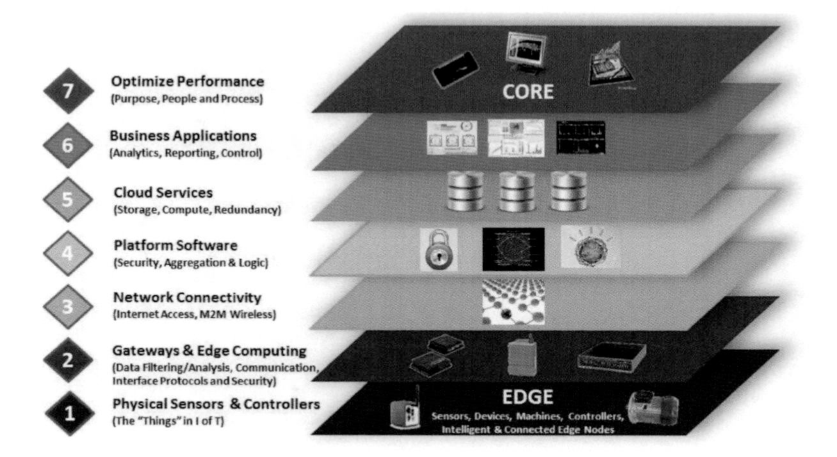

Failing to Use a Structured IoT Planning Methodology

Internet of Things implementation projects are similar to many types of projects conducted in your organization. However, the scope and scale of IoT projects are often much larger than anything organizations have attempted previously. It is critical to use an IoT planning framework that takes this complexity into account as shown in this diagram:

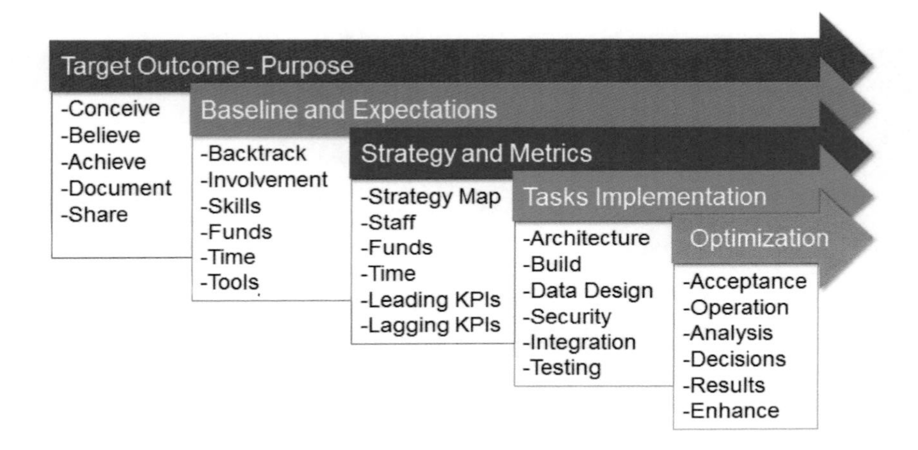

You can see this IoT planning process is structured as follows:

IoT Target Outcome and Purpose - for your IoT network and documenting your IoT Vision in detail.

Baseline and Expectations - identify your current state of your IoT Target Area and discover how to reach your Target Value. Discuss and negotiate all your IoT stakeholder expectations. Data shows that missed expectations often doom IoT projects.

Strategy and Metrics – using your Baseline and Backtrack analysis you build your StratGraph to go from your Current Value to your Target Value by your Target Date. Create all your IoT Key Performance Indicators and success criteria.

TASKs Implentation – document all the tasks that need to be accomplished to realize your IoT deployment. TASK stands for: Time, Accountability, Steps and Keep score.

Optimization – drive change in your orgnization and acheive your IoT Target Outcome with a high ROI IoT implementation.

#3 – Not Collecting Baseline Information

Researching and Documenting your Current State

Once you have your IoT Target Outcome and decided on your Planning Methodology, you need to conduct a baselining exercise to determine and document all your current IoT-related processes, legacy data creation and data storage mechanisms. You will Baseline in 3 main areas:

- Infrastructure, Data, and Operational Intelligence
- Security – both physical and data
- Resources – Skills, Staff, Finances, Technology, Culture

Begin your Baselining process:

1. Identify the Root Causes of the Gap between your IoT Target Outcome Current Value and Target Value.
2. Document how the Current Value is measured, data stored, analysis conducted and metrics reported.
3. Identify the people responsible for manual data collection, storage, and analysis.
4. Document your current Operations Technology, Information Technology, and Operational Intelligence infrastructure.
5. Identify Root Cause indicators and drivers. Use "5 Whys" methods to determine what sensors should be implemented to create the data that will be collected and analyzed to solve the Root Cause(s).
6. Start working up the IoT Reference Model from the Sensor level and document the current situation at each level.
7. Build the Root Cause solution scenario from your Baseline information. When you hit a dead-end, use the Backtrack method.

Using Backtrack Method for Baselining

In order to collect comprehensive Baseline information as the foundation for your IoT Strategy and Tasks Plan, you must use a discovery process that utilizes a two directional method of inquiry. This diagram shows how you start with Today's Current State and work toward your Target Outcome. Then you start with your Target Outcome and work backwards using "5-Whys" and "Why-How-What" questions.

#4 – Underestimate Difficulty,Skills,Time, Costs

Internet of Things deployments are complex. As we discussed in Mistake #2, there are many technologies, software applications, networks, security protocols and new business processes that must be combined to realize IoT success. This complexity means your organization must understand this complexity, identify the skills you need, your project schedule and budget.

You must ask and answer the following questions about your organization. Ask "Do we have:"

1. Program Management for complex IoT system deployment?
2. Wireless Sensor Networking Protocol skills?
3. Hardware development for Sensors, Gateways, etc.?
4. Embedded Systems/Firmware expertise?
5. Mobile networking and endpoint management expertise?
6. Secure data expertise and programmers?
7. Software developers for IoT Software Platforms
8. Cloud data storage and virtual serve expertise?
9. Data analytics scientists and programmers?
10. Business Application Software programmers and integrators?

To Estimate your IoT Business Readiness you must document:

- IoT Skills and Disciplines that are lacking
- IoT Skills and Disciplines that need improvement
- IoT Skills and Disciplines that are strengths

Understanding IoT Impact on Your Entire Organization

We looked at the skills and knowledge your organization must have to implement a successful IoT solution. But IoT will impact almost every organization in your company as well as your corporate culture. The following diagram highlights all the organization areas where you will have to estimate IoT skills, time and costs.

Estimating the Impact on Your Culture

IoT is a means to an end. You are going to implement IoT to transform your business through Business Process Optimization or Market Differentiation. In either case, change needs to happen to realize your IoT Target Financial Return. First you will need to assess your current Organizational Culture. Then you need to map your IoT Target Outcome to your Culture to understand mis-matches and estimate the costs associated with how your Culture either embraces or rejects change.

#5 – Not Understanding Your IoT Stakeholders

Most Projects Fail due to People not Technology!

Many of us can look back at failed projects in our careers and identify the reasons for failure. The Calleam Consulting group reviewed 100's of failed projects for consistent themes. They found 8 Common Classes and mapped these in the following diagram:

People are the Main Theme

The Calleam "Wheel of Failure" highlights many areas where expectations were miscommunicated and/or misunderstood: Teamwork, Voice of Customer, Planning, Leadership, Underestimation (Mistake #4), Quality, Risk and Competency. To avoid IoT Project failure, the following steps should be pursued:

Step 1 – Identifying All Your IoT Stakeholders

As we saw in Mistake #4 there are many IoT Stakeholders inside your organization. Also, it is vital to document the expectations of your customers. Also document how your competition will respond to your IoT deployment.

Step 2 – Understanding Your Internal IoT Stakeholders

Identify the Lead Stakeholder in every department that will be touched by your IoT deployment and ask them the following and document their answers to use as rating information:

1. Do you agree with the IoT Target Outcome?
2. Is there a Positive or Negative impact to you from IoT?

3. How important is achieving IoT success?
4. Will you commit the resources required for IoT success?

Step 3 – Risk Assessment

You can now map your IoT Stakeholders status by their IoT Project support answers. The example IoT Stakeholder Heat Map shown below indicates that most IoT stakeholders are advocates, but there are several who do not support the IoT Project. At this point, you must address their concerns before you move on.

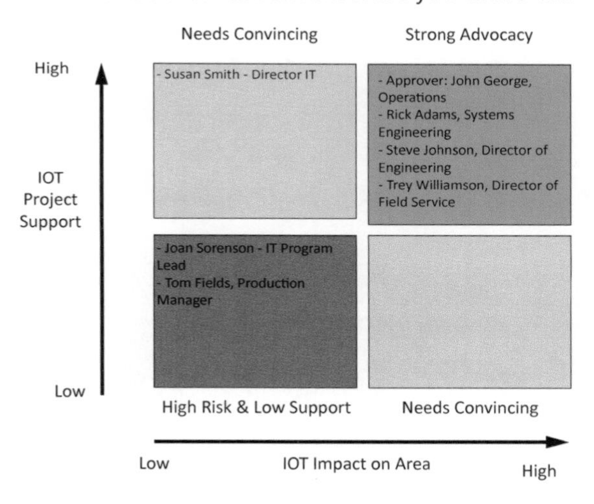

Step 4 - Customers and Competition

You should use your IoT Target Outcome Vision document to develop customer communication materials that work to identify your customer's pain points and explain how your IoT deployment will help them realize their success. You also use your IoT Target Outcome to assess competitive response - how competition might upset your IoT deployment, or how they will respond once you have realized IoT success.

#6 – Poorly Constructed Strategy Document

Creating Strategy is Difficult

Recall that in Mistake #5 we highlighted that Strategy was one of the 8 reasons for Project Failure. Many organizations struggle with creating a strategy that will drive their IoT Task Plan. Your Strategy document is the process you use to realize your IoT Target Outcome.

Your StratGraph

Strategy is best implemented as a graph that gets you from your Current State to your Target Outcome. Using your Baseline and Backtracking information, you create the paths that will drive your IoT Tasks plan. Your StratGraph will also have contingency routes if your primary path becomes blocked.

"All men can see these tactics whereby I conquer, but what none can see is the strategy out of which victory is evolved."

Sun Tzu

Key Components of StratGraph Construction

You create your IoT Target Outcome StratGraph using several key inputs:

1. Business Pain Points and Root Causes
2. Current and desired Key Performance Indicators
3. Baseline and Backtrack information
4. Expectations of all IoT Stakeholders
5. Skills assessment, make/buy analysis
6. Financial budget and constraints
7. Time line and resource availability
8. Identification of all Infrastructure to be IoT enabled

Need Contingency Plans

As you undertake your IoT journey using your StratGraph, unexpected things will happen. You need to create a StratGraph with alternate routes that will get you to your IoT destination. You do not need all the facts for your Plans B, C or D, but you should have these contingencies documented.

#7— Incomplete IoT TASKs Plan Without Accountabilities, Dates & Tracking Metrics

Constructing a Complete IoT Deployment TASKs Plan

Having created a robust IoT StratGraph, you can now layout the tasks required to realize your IoT deployment success. The phases of your IoT Tasks Plan will be:

1. Research
2. Procurement

3. Develop and Debug
4. Install and Integrate
5. Field/System Test
6. Data Generation
7. Business Optimization via Target Outcome Realization

TASK is an acronym

As will be described in the BEST System discussion, a Task has 4 parts: a time duration, accountable person responsible for the task achievement, steps to complete, and a results tacking scorecard.

T = Time - a Task has a specific start date and duration assigned to it when the desired output of this task is to be realized

A = Accountability - a single person is accountable to get this Task done with the resources required for success documented.

S = Steps - these are the specific actions that must be taken to achieve the task.

K = Keep Score - create and use your IoT project schedule and scorecard that tracks all steps to be done by whom by when.

As your IoT Project moves through you TASKs plan, you will encounter issues and roadblocks. Recall that we planned for this with Contingency Routes in the IoT StratGraph. Your IoT Target Outcome should not be adjusted, adjust your action steps.

"When it is obvious that the goals cannot be reached, don't adjust the goals, adjust the action steps."

Confucius

IoT TASKs Plan Success Drivers

A successful IoT Implementation Plan depends on the following:

1. **Assumptions** - must resolve them to facts
2. **Alignments** - expectations must be aligned
3. **Accountabilities** - identify specific individuals who will own a particular Task.
4. **Agreements** - parties must agree with the IoT Target Outcome and commit to their IoT TASKs Plan deliverables

Remove IoT TASKs Plan Risk Using a Premortem Review

Use the Premortem Risk Assessment tool to analyze what can go wrong before you start your IoT project. Assemble your IoT Coalition team and identify all potential failure mechanisms and issues. Then go back and update your IoT StratGraph with contingency plans.

#8 – Failing to Transform IoT Data Into Actions That Optimize Business Performance

Your Ultimate IoT Goal = Business Transformation

Recall back in Mistake #3 we diagrammed your IoT Planning Process. We discussed why your IoT Target Outcome, Baseline, Expectations, Strategy and TASKs Plan are so vital. However please remember:

An IoT Deployment is only the Means to a Business Transformation End

Your IoT financial returns will be generated when your organization utilizes the generated IoT Data to realize your IoT Target Outcome.

Your IOT Target Outcome is the <u>Optimization</u> of an important facet of your business. *And it all happens here*

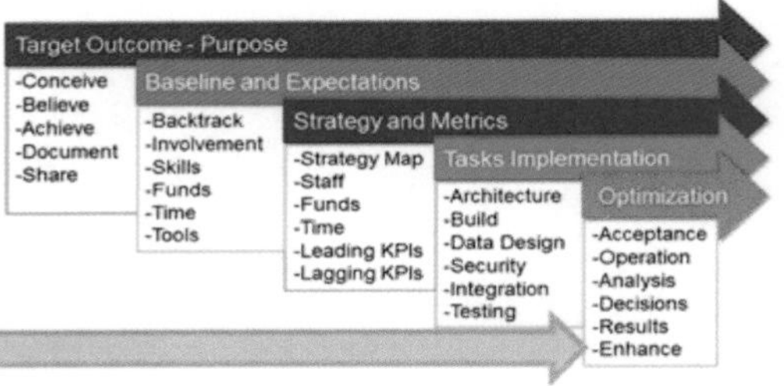

Driving Change Using a Complete IoT Business Case

Use an IoT Planning process that creates this important financial info:

1. Time Duration = Start to IoT Target Outcome Date
2. Target Outcome Return as $ New Revenues or Cost Savings
3. Gross Margin if Target Return is Revenues vs. profits
4. Total IoT Project cost from your IoT cost quotes and estimates
5. Number of years for IoT Project return calculation

6. Weighted Average Cost of Capital or the Discount rate used in NPV and IRR Calculations
7. IoT Financial Returns per Year for each of the years in the Return period
8. NPV - Net Present Value Calculation
9. IRR – Internal Rate of Return
10. Utilize these financial results in your IoT Business Case

Leveraging your IoT Deployment with New IoT Projects

Once you have successfully deployed your first IoT Project, you now have an excellent base upon which to create additional value in your organization:

- You have a proven IoT Planning Process that works for your company that has demonstrated a high Return on Investment.
- You can leverage your new IoT Platform to quickly and cost effectively add new IoT solutions that will create additional value at a high ROI.
- You will be able to combine information from your IoT deployments in innovative ways to create new insights, business processes and competitive advantages.

The 8 IoT Business Transformation System Success Steps

In order to avoid the 8 Deadly IoT Mistakes that can cripple your IoT deployment, here are the steps you should take:

1. IoT Target Outcome - your vision urgently driven by senior leadership
2. Baseline and Backtrack from Current Value to Target Value
3. Expectations of all IoT Stakeholders understood by IoT Coalition Team
4. Strategy that visualizes how you will achieve IoT success.
5. Tasks Plan with single point of accountabilities continuously communicated by your IoT Coalition
6. Blueprint and Deploy IoT solution implemented using milestones with short term wins that are celebrated
7. Change and Communicate - drive culture change, deploy new processes, celebrate wins, reward accountable team members

8. Anchor new Business Transformation processes become standard habit to drive IoT Target Outcome success

Focus on the Steps for IoT Success

Now knowing the 8 Key IoT Mistakes to Avoid, we can map out the systems, processes and techniques you will use to create your Internet of Things deployment success.

The IoTaudit System

Ask the Right Questions to Get the Right Answers...

The first IoT Business Transformation System process is the IoTaudit System. The IoTaudit is a framework-based tool suite designed to identify your key IoT business drivers, help you avoid expensive mistakes, and create your optimal IoT solution. The output of the IoTaudit creates important information for the next three processes.

There are several key philosophies embedded in the IoTaudit:

- Internet of Things sensors are essentially a way to create "Infrastructure Data" that is typically inaccessible.
- This new IoT sensor data will be combined and analyzed with some of your existing data sources to provide new "Operational Intelligence" to realize your business transformation.
- Developing this ability to extract useful knowledge from new data sets needs to be considered a key corporate strategic asset that will enable additional business performance optimization.

Start with Business Pain Point and Financial Return

Your Internet of Things deployment must have a positive Return on Investment to be considered a successful business transformation. You should be able to quantify the columns in this diagram:

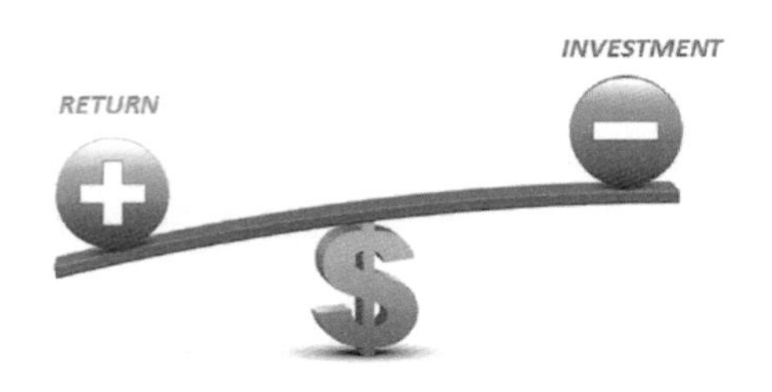

Save money	Hardware and Software Costs
Added Revenues	Network Costs
New Products/Services $	Cloud and Analytics Costs
New Business Models $	Staff Costs
Added Market Share $	Install and Maintain Costs

Using Financial Return calculations will allow your organization to then review the IoT costs in light of this return. You are able to make an educated IoT Project financials Go/No Go decision at this point.

Identifying your IoT Industry Areas

As we reviewed earlier, Internet of Things solutions can be utilized in many different types of industries. We have not have not found a single industry that cannot be served by IoT to some advantage.

Industries such as Aerospace, Agriculture, Chemicals, Computers, Construction, Defense, Education, Energy, Entertainment, Financial, Food, Government, Healthcare, Hospitality, Manufacturing, Mass Media, Telecommunications, Transportation and Water.

The following chart highlights many applications - is yours listed?

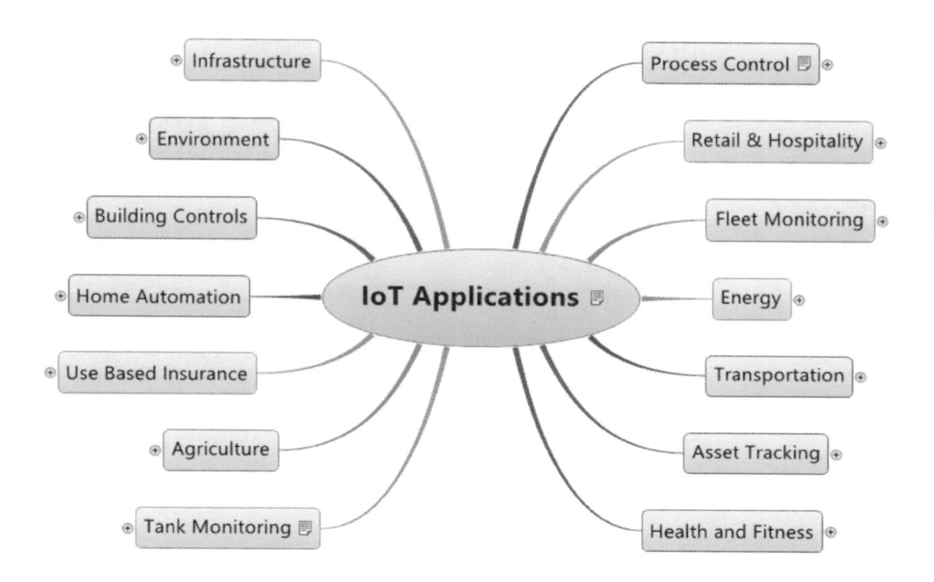

Applications Within All Industries

Across every Industry there are types of applications that can be enhanced with IoT. One of these could be your IoT Target Outcome Target Area. Here are several examples:

- Predictive Maintenance – when and how a device might fail, what parts and skills are needed to preemptively fix.
- Loss Prevention – monitor device status and network usage to flag unusual usage that may indicate revenue loss/theft
- Asset Utilization – monitor and predict assets to improve asset, device and sensors utilization.
- Inventory Tracking – monitor levels to minimize loss and waste. Improve inventory utilization, increase inventory turns.
- Disaster Planning and Recovery – monitor important and sensitive equipment to alert personnel and trigger intervention procedures.
- Downtime Minimization – predictive maintenance and inventory tracking to identify parts and personnel.

- Energy Usage Optimization - monitor current, voltage, lighting, occupancy, temperature and humidity to optimize energy use.
- System Performance Effectiveness - monitor equipment over time to determine life-cycle trends and highlight variances.
- Network Performance Management - monitor traffic flows, equipment utilization and security breaches.
- Capacity Utilization - monitor performance of individual sub-systems, systems, and overall process to determine optimal use.
- Yield Management - systems are instrumented to determine areas of Yield loss and preventive measures to reduce equipment downtime.
- Capacity Planning - with Utilization and Yield Recovery data, process capacity can be calculated and managed.
- Demand Forecasting - Monitoring the systems that drive demand are compared to Capacity Planning data for resource optimization
- Load Balancing Optimization - with Capacity, Yield and Demand data the loads placed across systems can be balanced.
- Pricing Optimization - using Demand and Capacity IoT to optimize equipment and process costs, variable Pricing can be optimized.

IoTaudit Uses the BEST System

The IoTaudit uses the BEST System as its core framework as you can see in the following diagram. As will be explained in the next chapter, it is vital to utilize a system that will provide a coherent and coordinated methodology for your IoT data collection project.

The first step of the IoTaudit is to identify your business performance challenges and pain points that might be solved and optimized by an IoT implementation. Then you will prioritize these business areas by the amount of potential financial return and then create your IoT Target Outcome Statement:

"We will improve Target Area from Current Value to Target Value by Target Date that will achieve the Target Financial Amount."

We will explore how to use BEST System to create your Strategy and IoT Implementation Task Plan. When you use the IoTaudit Tools you will create:

1. Written business performance optimization IoT Target Outcomes with key performance metric targets
2. A complete Baseline of your IoT applications, status, requirements technology, skills and readiness
3. An understanding of the Expectations of all the parties involved in your IoT deployment – internal and external
4. Your IoT StratGraph – what is the process, resources, and timeline for rolling out your IoT Deployment

5. Your IoT Implementation Task list for all the actions and accountabilities.
6. IoT Business Transformation deliverables.

IoTaudit System Tools, Website and Instructional Videos

The IoTaudit System was created as both a Do-it-Yourself tool suite and the basis for the IoTaudit Discovery Workshop. Details on the IoTaudit System are available here: http://enviro-controls.com/iotaudit-system/.

An extensive IoTaudit System video library is available at no charge on the IoTaudit website: http://www.iotaudit.com/.

Now let's explore the BEST System in detail.

The BEST System

Build Your IoT Plans on a Solid Foundation...

The BEST System is a powerful but simple way to solve problems and achieve goals of all sorts – large or small – professional or personal. The BEST System is used as the foundational framework for the IoTaudit. But you will find you can use the BEST System in all areas of your life. It may be trying to get a project team organized and effective at work. Or you may be focused on improving sales for your business. It is even handy in motivating your kids to do something you would like them to do. (Unfortunately, my kids now know when they are being BEST-System'd). The BEST System can scale from very small goals to very large goals depending on the techniques you use in each BEST System phase.

The BEST System came about from an unlikely source. I had been a Cub Scout leader for many years in Minnesota and one day seven-year-old Brandon came up to me. He tugged on my pants leg and asked "Mr. Grady you always say in meetings Do your Best. But how do I do my best?" It kind of stopped me in my tracks. I hemmed and hawed a bit and said, "you should identify your goal, and the problems you will have reaching that goal, figure out what you need to do, apply the scouting skills we taught you, and keep trying until you reach your goal." Well, he looked at me rather quizzically and wandered off. I realized of course my explanation wasn't particularly good. So I started to think about how could I provide a better answer using a simple and systematic approach for to how to "Do your Best."

A few weeks later, I was in looking out the window in the Aloft hotel while attending a technical trade show outside Chicago. I was doodling the letters B,E,S,T while considering all the management and motivational techniques I had been learned over several decades.

All of a sudden my subconscious kicked in and the BEST System concept came to me. Here is what I wrote on the Aloft notepad (this is indeed the actual photo - what would we do without smartphones...)

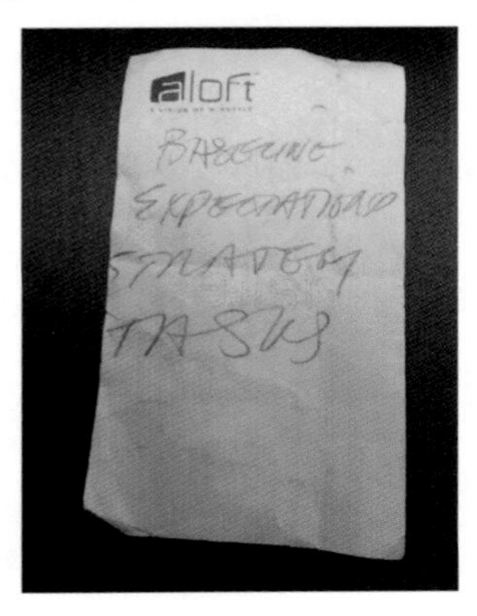

As you can see the B stands for Baseline, E stands for Expectations, S stands for Strategy, and T stands for Tasks. I thought wow – I think this meets the Brandon test!

So now I had a problem solving process, but I needed to create the way to clearly state the goal to be achieved. It was important this statement be clear, concise, concrete and have a definite purpose. The word goal tends to be somewhat ambiguous and always leaves the impression of aspiration but not specific achievement. In his famous 1937 book Think and Grow Rich, Napoleon Hill uses the term "chief aim". This is better than goal as it provides a sense of priority and urgency. But aim suggests where you are pointed, not providing a vivid vision of success. So I chose the term Target Outcome for a very specific set of reasons. Target Outcome combines the targeting "this where am I aiming" with the definite "this is exactly what I want to accomplish". Now we can combine Target Outcome and BEST into this BEST System diagram.

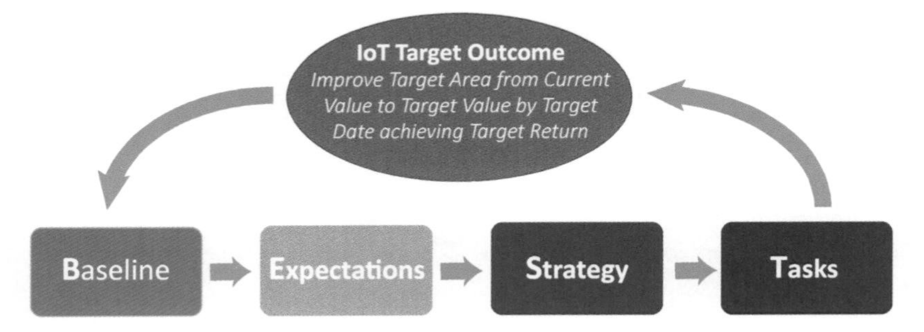

The BEST System is a powerful process with these attributes:

- Simple – a 5 process steps
- Scalable – the BEST System can be used with any size project, or problem at any level of complexity
- Easy to remember
- Easy to implement
- Easy to teach to others in your organization
- Easy to visualize the Target Outcome and obtain results

The BEST System also provides a common language across your IoT Project Team and IoT Stakeholders.

- Successful Teams all use a common language.
- Sports teams have perfected using a common language – often with encrypted terms.
- Common language has to be enforced by the IoT Team Leader. That's why you generate your IoT Target Outcome, Strategy and Tasks Plan.
- Common language is often used in technical professions – medicine, engineering, etc. But often common language for Projects and solving daily problems is not taught in school, in organizations, or in companies.
- The BEST System is simple, easy to communicate, easy to embrace, and easy to put into practice

Let's examine each of the BEST System components.

Your Target Outcome is the Achievement you Want to Tangibly Realize

The words "tangibly realize" were chosen very carefully in the Target Outcome definition. The Target Outcome must be something that is not virtual or soft - not a goal, not a yearning, not a desire. You absolutely must be able to visualize and describe your Target Outcome in great detail – what does it Look like? Feel like? Even Sound Like - Taste Like - Smell Like?

As will be explained in the next Chapter, your IoT Target Outcome will be constructed as:

"We will improve our Target Area from the Current Value to the Target Value by the Target Date achieving the Target Financial Return."

You can see this IOT Target Outcome Statement meets all our criteria: clear, concise, concrete and have a definite purpose. You will use your IoT Target Outcome with all your IoT Project Stakeholders. You will document in detail the vision of your IoT Target Outcome so it can be effectively communicated to everyone. To realize your IoT business transformation success, you must over-communicate in order to drive change. The following quote is the basic tenet of your Target Outcome:

What Your Mind Conceives,
And Your Heart Believes,
You Can Achieve

Napoleon Hill, Muhammad Ali,
Jesse Jackson and other successful leaders

You must completely believe that you will achieve Target Outcome and nothing can stand in your way. It is this fervent belief in your success that will cause others to enlist and support your Target Outcome. Many people, project teams and companies start out with great intentions but wind up failing to reach their Target Outcome because they did not really believe they could achieve it. The famous quote from Henry Ford "If you believe you can or you believe you can't - you're right" is especially applicable. Your ability to "paint the picture" of how your Target Outcome is important to others will dictate much of your success. This positive belief in making your Target Outcome happen will bring people along with you in support of your TO. That is why we spend so much time articulating and putting together the details around the IoT Target Outcome. It sets up everything else that follows with the Best System.

Once your Target Outcome is firmly established and documented, we use the BEST System to make it happen. The BEST System is composed of 4 steps:

B is for Baseline

Baselining is the process of understanding all the issues, attributes and surrounding information concerning your Target Outcome. You will identify very specifically the Who, What , Where, Why and most importantly When. It is an assessment of the landscape you will encounter on your journey to a successful Target Outcome.

Baselining takes a lot of work. Many people do not have the patience to do baselining well. Also, good baselining tools are not readily available which complicates the task. The concept of Backtracking will be introduced in the IoTaudit Baselining chapter that helps bridge your Current Value to your Target Value, Target Date and Target Return.

E is for Expectations

This step is to identify, negotiate and document the expectations of all your IoT Project stakeholders. Your management, peers, subordinates, IoT Project Team, IoT Stakeholders, your Customers and your Competitors. Many projects fail because expectations of stakeholders where not understood. Making assumptions is often the cause of failure. So it is vital to identify everyone associated with your IoT Project and have a discussion with them about your IoT Target Outcome, how this TO will affect them (positively and negatively), solicit and in some cases negotiate their support, and document the results.

You should be able to visualize how all the stakeholders behave upon achievement of your Target Outcome. Some will be happy (the more the better), but some will be unhappy especially in competitive business situations. But understanding your stakeholder behaviors through the course of realizing your Target Outcome will dramatically influence the next two BEST System steps.

S is for Strategy

Now that you have done your initial Baseline Assessment and Expectation Investigation, you have enough data to create the Strategy that achieves your desired Target Outcome. The StratGraph tool is used to visualize your strategic journey from today to a successful Target Outcome. Strategies will scale depending on the nature and size of the Target Outcome. Your StratGraph will show your success path, but also have contingencies that might arise along the way. Seldom do things go exactly as planned and we need to create multiple routes to success.

At this point in the process you have done three critical steps that many people never do well - baseline the situation, document the expectations of all the IoT stakeholders, and formulate a strategy using the facts found in your Baseline and Expectation analyses. Using this information you will build your plan that will describe - Where, When, Why, What and the resources required to accomplish the What. What is the last of the four BEST System steps – Tasks.

T is for Tasks

The word Tasks was chosen very specifically. A task has several attributes that a Step, which just identifies the particular action to be taken, does not. A task has a duration, resources who are accountable for the task achievement, and action steps.

BEST System and the IoT Business Transformation System

You can see how the BEST System is a simple yet powerful foundation for the IoT Business Transformation System. Additionally, because the BEST System is easy to remember and implement, it will eventually become a habit. After a while, you will put the BEST System to work subconsciously. As you employ the BEST System, others around you will be influenced by your approach. They will begin to use the BEST System without realizing that they are using a powerful systematic way to get things done.

Using the BEST System as our IoT Planning Framework, let's get to work creating your specific IoT Target Outcome that will drive your business transformation success.

IoT Target Outcome

Conceive and Believe to Achieve...

The first step in using the BEST System is to create your IoT Target Outcome (we will often reference this as TO for short). You will develop a complete vision of your TO and document it in great detail.

When creating your Target Outcome it's very important to understand how to position and describe your TO. Many companies often say: "we want to be the market leader", or "generate more profits", or "raise our customer satisfaction". Without being specific, your IoT efforts will never be optimized.

It is vital that you're able to describe your IoT Target Outcome in great detail to others. There have been many business studies that show that miscommunication of the ultimate goal (Target Outcome) is the fundamental reason projects struggle and companies fail. Even back in the 1960s, a Stanford University study analyzed data from Fortune 500 companies and found that a 35% discrepancy between the company's objectives and what was actually implemented. The problem was not the employees were incompetent, but that the objectives were too ambiguous and many employees didn't know the true purpose of what they were doing.

Conceive Your IoT Target Outcome

Your IoT Target Outcome = the successful attainment of your Business Transformation using an Internet of Things Deployment.

You will write down your Target Outcome in great detail. Documenting the TO gives you a feeling of commitment and is incredibly useful when interacting with everyone around you. The better you can describe your Target Outcome to others, the more successful you will be.

The IoT Target Outcome Format

Your IoT Target Outcome statement takes the following form:

"We will improve our Target Area from Current Value to Target Value by Target Date achieving the Target Financial Return"

Here are some IoT Target Outcome examples:

We will improve on-time customer shipments from 95% to 99.9% by Dec 31, 2017 achieving $500,000 new revenues.

We will improve weekly machine uptime to from 90% to 97% by June 1, 2017 achieving $800,000 in combined maintenance savings and additional revenues.

We will improve inventory shrinkage from 5% to 2% by October 1, 2017 achieving a $2.5 million cost savings.

The key IoT Target Outcome statement requirements are:

1. Your Target Area which is a very specific business pain point.
2. Your Current Value in currency, %, technical units, etc.
3. Your Target Value in the same currency, %, technical units, etc.
4. Your Target Date is a specific Month, Day, Year. Not a quarter, or planning period that has wiggle room. Your IoT Project Team and IoT Stakeholders need an actual date for visualization and urgency.
5. Your Target Return will be in currency only. Not a percent, ratio, "goodness level", or other value. It is critical that you calculate the monetary return for your IoT Implementation right from the start. You will use this Target Return in your IoT Business Case Return on Investment (ROI) calculation.

"We Will..."

The first two words of any Target Outcome, "We will..." were chosen very carefully. There are several things implied here. "We" implies that it will take a team to produced this Target Outcome. This is universally true for any Target Outcome that drives business transformation. "Will" is the definite positive affirmation that your team will succeed. Words like "Plan","Hope","Our Strategy", etc. are never used.

"Improve"

In almost all Target Outcomes the word used after "We will" is improve. Improve says to your IoT stakeholders we will make things better. I found a curious fact about the word *Improve* on www.dictionary.com: "In the early 16th century (as emprowe or improwe) was from the Anglo-Norman French *emprower* (based on Old French *prou* 'profit,' ultimately from Latin *prodest* 'is of advantage'); -owe was changed to -ove under the influence of *prove*. The original sense was 'make a profit, increase the value of'; subsequently 'make greater in amount or degree.' This definition provides a historic sense of empowerment, profit, advantage, and increased value.

When we sit down with our clients to construct an IoT Target Outcome, we always try to use the word Improve in their Target Outcome. However, there are situations where another verb works well. Reduce can be a powerful word in conjunction with safety, security or health. "We will reduce the number of deadly illnesses from tainted water from 12,000 per year to 0 per year by December 31, 2018 resulting in $10 million medical cost savings." I realize this TO is a bit dark, but you get the point. The stakeholders in this TO can all share a compelling vision of no one dying. The key is to choose an action verb that inspires your IoT Stakeholders.

Choosing your Target Area

Your IoT Target Outcome Target Area must focus on a critical Business Pain Point. You Target Area selection is a crucial decision. Solving this Business Pain Point should be worth all the hard work, money, time, staff, and resources that will be required to implement your IoT solution. So to that end you may want to create more than one Target Outcome with different Target Areas to compare and contrast importance.

These are excellent starting points for IoT Target Area:

- Business Pain Points
- Under-performing Key Performance Indicators
- Important issues your Leaders are grappling with now
- Customer Responsiveness and/or Retention
- Supply Chain Logistics
- Product Quality
- Operational Efficiencies
- New Products and/or Services

- New Revenues
- Increase Margins
- Increase Return on Working Capital
- Budget Efficiencies
- Regulatory Compliance
- Safety
- Security
- Employee Productivity and/or Collaboration
- New Business Models

Target Area Focused on a New Product or New Service

Your key Business Pain Point might be to drive new revenues through a unique competitive advantage. Smart Connected Product vendors can develop Internet of Things capabilities to create a new product or service to drive Market Differentiation. Target Area selection might be:

- Identify new product features and benefits that can be introduced through adding IoT capabilities.
- How can existing product performance be improved by adding new sensor/control devices and analysis.
- New Services can be created by collecting IoT Infrastructure Data and providing Alarming, Monitoring and Predictive Analysis data.
- Target Area Focused on Customers
- Most customer related IoT initiatives involve new revenue creation and might include areas such as:
- Improve Customer Experience
- Introduce new products/features for greater wallet share
- Enhance the value chain to increase Satisfaction
- Provide compelling value to insure repeat purchases
- Enable new ways for Customers to refer you to New Customers
- Leverage IoT capabilities to create and introduce:
- Access new Geographies and Markets
- Introduce New Business Models

Current Value

Your IoT Target Outcome Current Value is the current status of your Target Area expressed in a unit of measure. This might be a yield percentage, quality control metric, process throughput, market share, revenue dollars, supply chain efficiency, etc.

Target Value

Your IoT Target Outcome Target Value is the desired improvement from your Current Value expressed in the same unit of measure as Current Value.

Target Date

This is the specific Month Day Year when your organization will realize your IoT Target Outcome Target Value and Target Financial Return.

Target Return

This is the is the financial return you expect to receive when your realize your IoT Target Outcome. It is expressed in the currency of your choice. Other units of measure are not acceptable. The Target Return number will be used in your IoT Business Transformation Return on Investment calculation.

Target Financial Returns can be achieved from

- New profits from service models that have recurring revenues.
- Optimize manufacturing costs and efficiencies in operations.
- Deliver new customer experiences via anything-as-a-service.

Constructing Your IoT Target Outcome

Using these building blocks, you can now assemble your IoT Target Outcome. Try several of your key business pain points. Then choose one of your Target Outcome statements for the Vision process.

Documenting your Target Outcome Vision

The next important step is to document your Target Outcome in great detail. You describe your Target Outcome from the perspective of your Team, your Company, your Customers, your Suppliers, and your Stakeholders. You won't your IoT Implementation approach yet as these you will come through the Baseline and Expectations phases as you build your StratGraph and TASKs plan.

Target Outcome Vision Techniques

First you will create a 3-5 page Target Outcome Vision (TOV) document on your own. This will provide you with a first draft for your TOV session with your IoT Coalition Project Team. You start by just brainstorming all the facets surrounding your Target Outcome. Here are some starter topics - feel free to add/delete in your list:

- What does your IoT success look like? Paint the scene in detail. Envision celebrations and awards.
- Who is Involved in the success? IoT Project Team, IoT Stakeholders, Target Area staff, Internal departments, Partners, Suppliers, Customers, etc.
- What do people say? CEO, Board of Directors, Senior leaders, your Supervisor, Peers, Subordinates, Customers, Investors, Press, Industry Analysts, Investors, Competitors, etc.
- Target Area Changes - Target Value Achievement, New Processes and Procedures, Removed Processes and Procedures
- Technology - Sensors, Network, Software, Data Analysis
- Security - Physical, Data, Users
- Finance- Target Return, Capital Outlay, Expenses, Business Case ROI
- Employees - New Team Members, New Skills, New Employee Assignments, New Organizational Structure
- Culture Change - New Habits, New Attitudes, Acceptance of Business Transformation.
- Market Reaction - Market Differentiation, Market Share Change, Competitive Response

As you will see in other parts of this book, I like to use Xmind tools to create mind maps. The following Target Outcome Vision mind map lists all the topics in the previous bullets. Using mind maps is an excellent way to brainstorm your projects and visually communicate complex topics. Xmind software standard version is free and this mind map can be downloaded for your use at www.enviro-controls.com/iottransform.

70% of the population are visual learners and this quote ties into your IoT Target Outcome Vision document:

The soul never thinks without a picture.

Aristotle

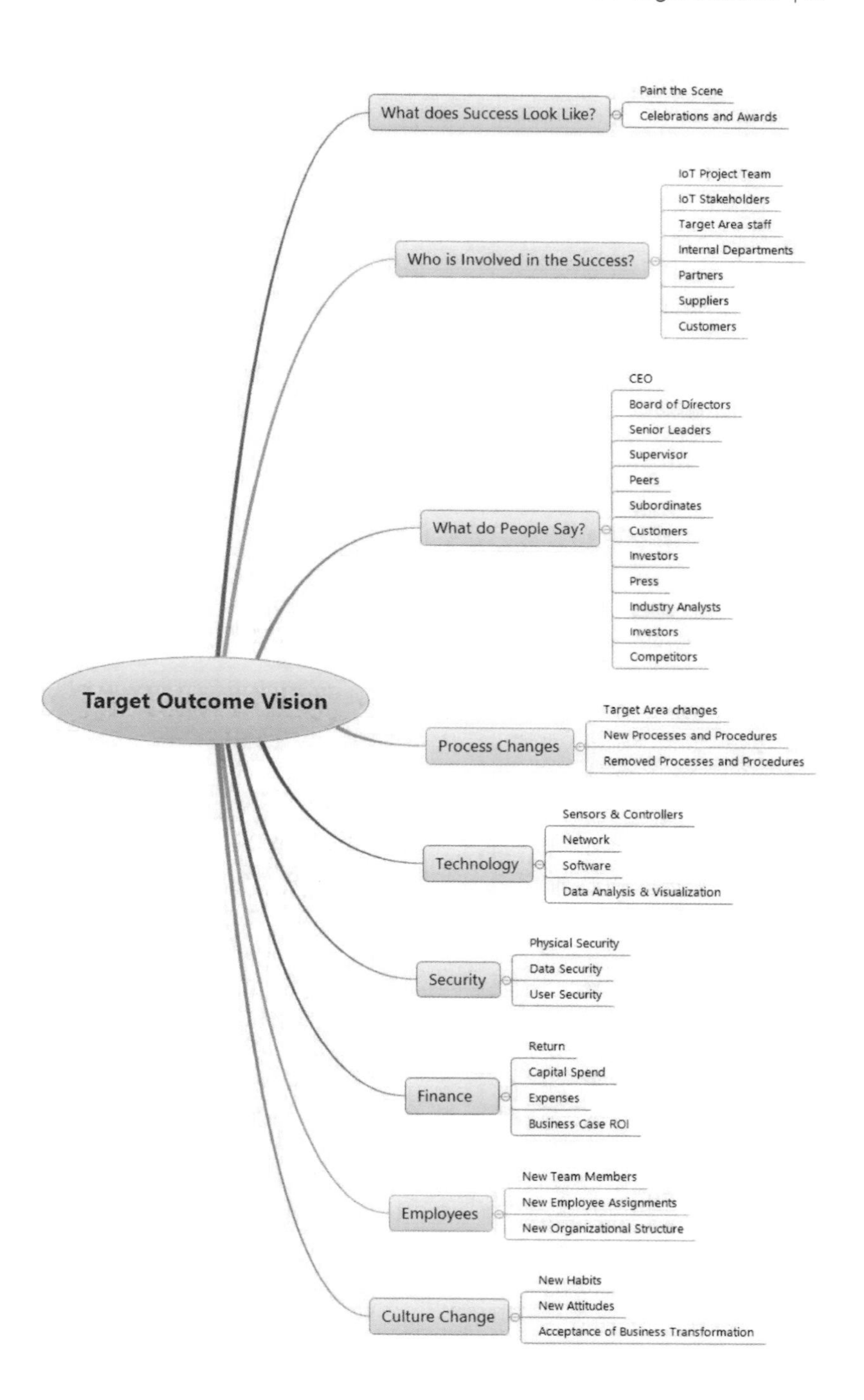
Target Outcome Vision
What does Success Look Like?
Paint the Scene
Celebrations and Awards
Who is Involved in the Success?
IoT Project Team
IoT Stakeholders
Target Area staff
Internal Departments
Partners
Suppliers
Customers
What do People Say?
CEO
Board of Directors
Senior Leaders
Supervisor
Peers
Subordinates
Customers
Investors
Press
Industry Analysts
Investors
Competitors
Process Changes
Target Area changes
New Processes and Procedures
Removed Processes and Procedures
Technology
Sensors & Controllers
Network
Software
Data Analysis & Visualization
Security
Physical Security
Data Security
User Security
Finance
Return
Capital Spend
Expenses
Business Case ROI
Employees
New Team Members
New Employee Assignments
New Organizational Structure
Culture Change
New Habits
New Attitudes
Acceptance of Business Transformation

Now you have created your IoT Target Outcome Statement and created your Target Outcome Vision document. Next you need to test these documents by doing the following:

1. Read your IoT Target Outcome out loud several times and make sure it sounds credible and authentic. If it sounds outlandish or unbelievable, you will not be able to convince your IoT Coalition Project Team or IoT Stakeholders to support you.
2. Print out your Target Outcome and tape it to the wall. Look at it as much as your can to internalize your success.
3. Read your Target Outcome Vision document out loud as you might in a conference room full of your team members. Similar your Target Outcome Statement, your TOV needs to be inspiring, motivating, drive real value for your organization and be beneficial to your IoT Stakeholders.
4. Next assemble a group of 3-6 people who will be key members of your IoT Coalition project team. Read your Target Outcome Statement and Target Outcome Vision document out loud to them. Discuss their reactions and enlist their suggestions.
5. Integrate the feedback from your team into an updated IoT Target Outcome and TOV document.

The next step in the BEST System is to Baseline your situation relative to your Target Area and the gap between your Current Value and your Target Value. Completely understanding your IoT Deployment landscape is the foundation on which you will build your IoT Strategy and TASKs Plan.

Baseline Your IoT Status

Understand the Terrain Before Your Attack...

You have identified and documented your IoT Target Outcome. Now we will Baseline all the issues surrounding your IoT Implementation. This fact finding process will provide the essential information that will be used to build your Strategy and IoT Implementation Plan. We will walk through a lengthy list of questions that will help you understand and document all the issues, attributes, and important information related to your IoT Target Outcome. You will identify very specifically the: Who, What, Where, Why and importantly When. Recall the BEST system diagram.

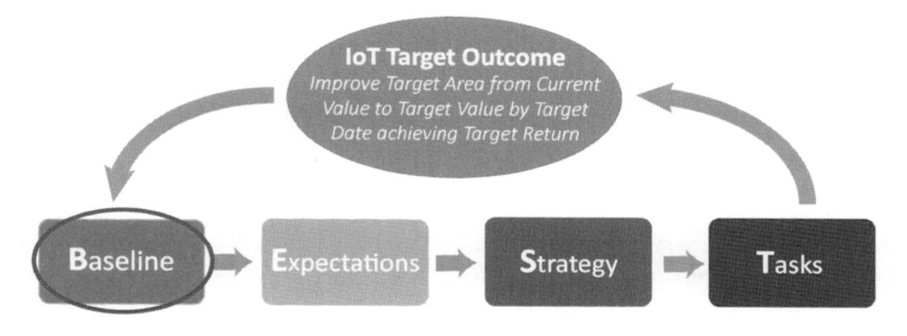

Baselining takes work. Many people skimp on this step. Think about the times you said to yourself, "If only we had thought this through completely, our project probably would not have failed".

The Baseline process is essential to realizing a successful IoT Target Outcome. Let's review the key elements of your IoT Target Outcome as these drive many elements of the Baseline process:

1. *IoT Target Area* – The business pain point area you plan to optimize with IoT needs to be fully described and

documented so your all your IoT stakeholders understand what process or market differentiation is to be changed.

2. *Primary Issues Related to Target Area* – Describe the issues surrounding your Target Area. For example, if your Target Area is Manufacturing Equipment uptime, the issues might be: "We cannot determine when equipment needs servicing in order to prevent breakdowns that halt production".
3. *Current Value* – Identify and document the current value and state of your Target Area. The units of the Current Value can be any appropriate metric.
4. *Target Value* - Identify and document the Target Value and state of your Target Area. This value can be any appropriate metric in the same units as your Current Value.
5. *Value Gap Root Cause Analysis* – Brainstorm all the root causes of the Gap between your Current Value vs. your Target Value. These Gaps are what will be solved using IoT technology, data generation, business transformation plans and change actions.
6. *Target Date* – Identify the specific Month, Day, Year your organization desires to achieve your Target Financial Return. Your Target Date provides the urgency need to drive your IoT Target Outcome.
7. *Target Financial Return* - Qualify and Quantify your Target Return monetary estimate. This financial return can be realized from various sources: cost savings, new revenues, profits, sale of assets, sale of financial instruments, etc.

Current Value to Target Value Gap Root Cause Identification

A key element of the Baseline process is to identify the root causes of the gap between your IoT Current Value and your IoT Target Value in your Target Outcome statement. Once these root causes are identified and documented, then we can work toward solving the gaps by using an Internet of Things solution.

Examples of root causes for the example Target Outcomes used in Chapter 6 might be:

- "We will improve on-time customer shipments from 95% to 99.9% by Dec 31, 2017 achieving $500,000 new revenues". The root causes could be: unexpected shipping line equipment breakdowns, packaging tracking issues, and/or inefficient use of delivery trucks

- "We will improve weekly machine uptime to from 90% to 97% by June 1, 2017 achieving $800,000 in combined maintenance savings and additional revenues." The root cause of the yield gap might be that 3 key machines in our lines have 30% unscheduled downtime, raw material flow delivery is inconsistent, and/or power fluctuations affect machine performance.
- "We will improve inventory shrinkage from 5% to 2% by October 1, 2017 achieving a $2.5 million cost savings" The root causes of this gap might be the inability to track the location and status of inventory, unable to identify everyone who comes in contact with the inventory, and/or inability to physically secure the inventory.

Solving Gap Root Causes

To identify the causes of the gap between your Current Value To Target Value, you need to ask a series of deep-dive questions such as:

- Can Root Cause #x be corrected and the Target Value achieved through the use of new alarms, alerts and reporting based on the Existing Infrastructure Data available?
- Using the Existing Infrastructure Data available for this Target Area, can Root Cause #x be corrected and the Target Outcome be achieved through the use of new methods, procedures or analysis and improving the Business Processes?
- Referring to any of the Manual Methods of obtaining Infrastructure Data, would the Target Value be attained if any or all of these manual processes were Automated?

Gap Root Cause – ID and OI Questions

The next questions pertain to adding NEW Infrastructure Data and Operational Intelligence to resolve the Root Cause #x of your gap:

- What NEW Operational Intelligence (OI) data and analytical capability would provide new insights into your gap.
- What alarms, alerts, events, notifications or other actions would be triggered by this OI data?
- What Analysis, Monitoring, Forecasting, Predictive and/or Prescriptive OI Analytics and Systems are necessary to implement the indicators and analysis mentioned in the above two questions?

- List the specific types and sources of the NEW Infrastructure Data to be combined with Existing Infrastructure Data to feed the New Operational Intelligence referred to above.

Baseline - Market Drivers

As you start your IoT Baseline activities, it is important to review the market drivers affecting your IoT Target Outcome and Target Area. You should collect data and understand the context of how each of the following areas affect your Target Outcome:

- Identify Target Area application market dynamics and document the 5 to 10 year future trends
- Collect and Document External and Internal Customer Requirements
- Competitor Status – what are they doing in relation to your Target Area. Are they using IoT to solve a similar problem?
- What is State of the Art in your Target Area. Identify new innovators and innovations.
- Industry – what are the industry-wide trends and technology trends. How do you become an industry leader?
- Government – understand Government positions, regulations and pending legislation.
- Economic Trends – identify positive and negative economic forces on your IoT Business Transformation.

Baseline Current Value Information Sources

Once you have documented your Target Area issues and identified the gaps be solved, you start to baseline Current Value-related information. Use Baseline questions pertaining to: current organizational processes, existing Infrastructure Data and Operational Intelligence in your Organization, current use of Sensors, M2M, Analytics and Operational Intelligence that comprise the current status of your Target Outcome Current Value.

Baseline IoT Target Outcome-related Organizational Processes

After understanding the Market Drivers affecting your IoT Target Outcome, you should look all the organizational processes that might be related to your IoT Business Transformation. Examining these processes reveals what Infrastructure Data and Operational Intelligence is currently produced and stored in each of these areas. Plan to examine the following areas at a minimum:

- Current Key Performance Indicators (KPIs) pertaining to your IoT Target Area and Current Value
- Efficiency Metrics
- Quality Metrics across all process stages
- Current Product Line Profit & Loss and margins where appropriate
- Manufacturing processes if appropriate
- Customer life-cycle and Go-To-Market processes
- Identify Network security capabilities, processes and protocols
- Identify Physical security capabilities and processes
- Specific legal requirements such as HIPAA, data privacy

Baseline Infrastructure Data and Operational Intelligence

Once you have identified and characterized all you IoT Target Outcome related organizational processes, you will baseline all your current Infrastructure Data. In order to understand the current state of your IoT Target Area you should implement these steps:

1. Document where data currently originates and how it is documented
2. Identify all current Infrastructure Data Sources
3. Identify relevant BI data related to the Target Outcome
4. Identify concurrent corporate data initiatives that might affect your Target Outcome.

Infrastructure Data is one of the fastest growing, most complex and valuable areas of big data: records of user transactions, customer behavior, device behavior, process status, environmental conditions, security threats, and fraudulent activity. Infrastructure Data is vitally important for IoT process optimization and business transformation..

Your current sources of Infrastructure Data might include;

- Application Logs
- Business Process Logs
- Call Detail Records
- Web Clickstream Data
- Configuration Files
- Database Audit Logs and Tables

- File System Audit Logs
- Management and Logging APIs
- Message Queues
- Network Incursions
- OS Metrics and Status
- Packet/Flow Data
- SCADA Data
- Sensors
- Syslog
- Web Access Logs
- Web Proxy Logs
- Wire Data
- Operational Intelligence

Document Infrastructure Data and Operational Intelligence

These are questions to ask to assemble your current state information:

- How does your Organization collect and calculate your Current Value - Briefly describe how your Organization creates the metric that is used to measure the current state for the Target Outcome Area.
- What business methods are used to create the Current Value? List any systems, software, processes or methods that are used to construct the number or value that represents the current status of the Target Outcome area (Metric) once the Operational Intelligence is assembled.
- What high-level information or Operational Intelligence is necessary to calculate the Current Value - List the information that is required to feed the processes and create Operational Intelligence associated with the Target Outcome Metric.
- What groups or departments in your Organization are responsible for taking the Operational Intelligence and constructing the Current Value? Specify the group in your Organization or Company that owns the task of creating and storing the Operational Intelligence associated with the Target Outcome Current Value.
- Where is the information stored so the business processes can have access for processing and generating the Target

Outcome Current Value? Describe the method of storing the Infrastructure Data that is critical to generate the metrics for the Target Outcome Current Value. Info could be in the Cloud, on a Server, or in some form of hard copy record.

Existing Automated Data Collection

Identify the existing systems that automatically collect, store, analyze and/or report data:

- What low-level systems, processes and methods are used to acquire the data necessary to create the Target Outcome Current Value?
- How is the existing Operating Information or Sensor Data aggregated before it is made available as Infrastructure Data for the Target Outcome Current Value? Identify whether this is an automatic or manual process.
- If automatic and/or electronic methods are used to collect information from machines and processes involved in the Target Outcome Current Value creation identify the specific source of the data.
- What automatic mechanisms are used to transport this information from equipment and processes to an access point or gateway prior to storage?
- Is there any automatically collected data from Sensors and/or the Infrastructure that drives the Current Value currently sent to internal servers or the Cloud?
- What Wide Area Network (WAN) connection scheme is currently used to provide the connection off premises to the next higher layer in the IoT Reference Model (Cloud)? Document the quantity for each connection type.
- What network providers are currently used for the WAN connection to the Cloud?
- What Cloud providers are currently used or preferred for Infrastructure Data storage?
- What processing or analytics are needed before the collected Infrastructure Data can be used as Operational Intelligence (OI) to form the Target Outcome Current Value?
- List any alarms, warnings, alerts or events that are triggered from the Infrastructure Data that also drives the Target Outcome Current Value.

- What is the estimated current expense for collecting ID, creating OI and utilizing this information to support the creation of the Target Outcome Current Value?

Baseline Using the IoT Reference Model

In order to effectively Baseline all the aspects of your IoT Project is useful to use the 7 layer IoT Reference Model shown in the following diagram. This model represents each major technology area from Sensors > Gateways > Network > IoT Services Software > Cloud Services > Business Application Software > Business Transformation . You are beginning to identify your IoT Network components at a high level by asking the question: "Can I use this technology to sense, transmit, store and or analyze the data needed to solve the root cause of the Gap?"

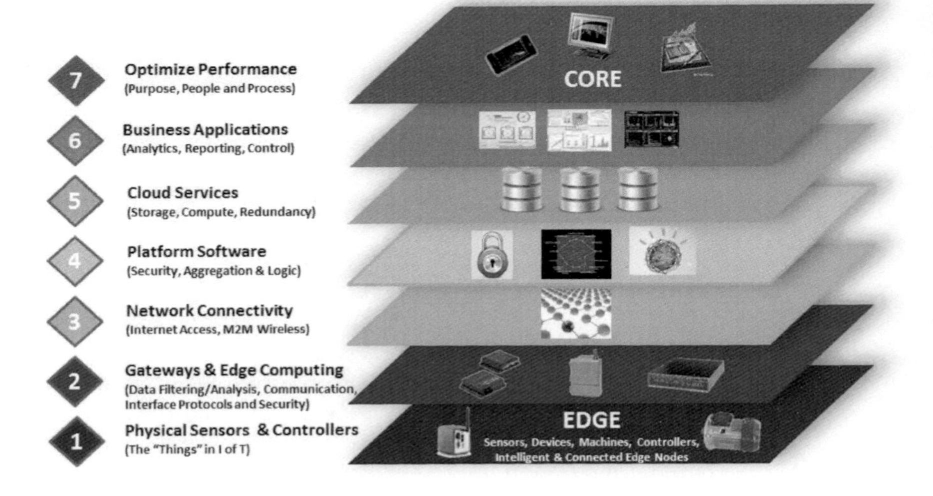

The lowest level of your IoT Network is where you will give a voice to uninstrumented infrastructure. You need to ask the following:

- If Sensors are to be used to acquire the information and data necessary to meet the Target Value, document the type of sensing modality and the potential quantity of each sensor.

- Is it necessary for the New Infrastructure Data to communicate with any existing systems in your company?

- Specify any special configurations, safety, environmental or physical implementation issues that may affect the installation or use of the IoT Sensor Network.
- Determine the each sensor's physical and installation attributes required to create your Infrastructure Data.
- The logistics of sensors that require attachment to machinery or inserted into flow needs to be identified and engineered
- The legacy system may need to be undisturbed and a "Smart Overlay" might be deployed

Layer 2 - Gateways and Sensor Interfaces

The next layer to Baseline is the Gateway requirements for Sensor LAN to Network WAN connectivity, management, data storage and computing.

- Approximately how often does the status of the machines or processes being monitored change?
- Approximately how often does data need to be collected and transmitted to the IoT Services Software to be useful?
- What is the accuracy requirements of each Sensor?
- Does the data transfer from Sensor to Gateway need to be Failsafe? Secure? Low Latency?
- What level of security is required in the LAN communications link between the new IoT Sensors and the Gateway?
- Can the data from some or all of the Sensors be consolidated at a common Gateway before being transmitted up to the next level of the IoT Reference Stack?
- Is there any data filtering or formatting that must be applied to the sensor data at the local level to make it conform to formatting requirements before it is transmitted to the Cloud?
- Are their any Edge Computing functions to be performed by the Gateway?

Layer 3 - Network Connectivity

The connectivity between Gateways and the IoT Services Software Platform is the next Baseline area. Investigate the following:

- Is connection to the Cloud necessary to correct this Root Cause and achieve the Target Value?
- What Wide Area Network (WAN) connection scheme is used to provide connection off premises from the Gateway to the next higher layer in the IoT Reference Model? List each connection type and the number of connections needed.
- What Network Providers are currently used or preferred for the WAN connection to the IoT Services Platform?

Layer 4 - IoT Services Software Platform

The IoT Services Software Platform is a critical component of your IoT Network. There are many functions provided at this layer. Ask:

- What Filtering, Aggregation, Conversion, Abstraction, Transaction & Security functions must be applied to the Infrastructure Data prior to database storage?
- What User Interface functions are required on the IoT Services Software Platform - network administration, maintenance, alarms, alerts, thresholds, data visualization, reports, and data analytics?
- What level of security is required in the WAN Layer between the Gateway and the IoT Services Software Platform?

Layer 5 - Cloud Storage and Applications

Cloud data storage, services and applications my be utilized as an intermediary between the IoT Services Software Platform and Business Applications software. Investigate the following:

- What Cloud provider(s) is(are) currently used or preferred for Infrastructure Data storage?
- Will Operational Intelligence analysis software run in the Cloud? If so, what applications?
- Will Operational Intelligence be stored in Private Servers?
- Will IoT-related Business Intelligence software applications run in the Cloud? On Private Servers?
- What level of Operational Intelligence Hierarchy will be used.

Layer 6 - Business Software Applications

Next you need to identify all the existing IT software systems and data stores that are relevant to your IoT Target Outcome. This includes:

- Financial Management
- Enterprise Reporting Programs
- Reporting and Analytics
- Service Management
- Purchasing and Supply Chain Management
- Warehouse Management
- Inventory Management
- Value Add Processing
- Order Management
- Customer Relationship Management

Manufacturing Operations Management Software Systems

MOM software systems are introduced over time often without an over-arching strategy. Your IT group may not be aware of all the MOM systems as they are often locally deployed and operated by manufacturing staff. You need to identify all the relevant MOM systems that pertain to your IoT Target Area and your Current Value. These MOM systems are usually segmented in the following 3 levels by domain and complexity.

MOM Level 1 – Industrial Automation and Machine Control

- Programmable Logic Control, Programmable Automation Control
- Industrial Process Control
- Motion Control
- Safety Monitoring
- Distributed Control Systems – DCS

MOM Level 2 – Manufacturing Management Systems

- Warehouse Management
- Document Management
- Configure, Model, Recovery Time Objective
- Enterprise Manufacturing Intelligence, History Reporting, Manufacturing Resource Planning

- Manufacturing Execution System, Tracking, Batch
- Time Tracking, Training, Operator Training Systems
- Statistical Process and Quality Control Hazard Analysis Critical Control Point
- Scheduling, Dispatching
- Asset Tracking
- Reliability-Centered Maintenance and Root Cause Analysis, Equipment Health
- Overall Equipment Effectiveness

MOM Level 3 – Enterprise and Business Operations Systems

- Enterprise Resource Planning, Advanced Planning and Optimization
- Customer Relationship Management, Customer Service Systems
- Product Line Management, Plant/Process Design, Business Process Management
- Environmental Health and Safety, Computerized Maintenance and Management System
- Business Intelligence, Supply Chain Management , Enterprise Quality Management Systems

Baseline Your Organization's Data Security

Document the following questions about Data Security as it pertains to the Target Outcome Current Value:

- How does the Organization measure the effectiveness of the Data Security today?
- Are facilities & locations physically secure where Infrastructure Data is currently collected to create the Target Outcome Current Value?
- Are facilities & locations secure where Operational Information (OI) is stored or processed to create the Target Outcome Current Value?
- What users typically have direct access to this collected and stored Infrastructure Data, Operational Intelligence and Applications?

- Do your Connected Assets receive command and control data as well as send information?
- Are data communications connections between machines or processes (Sensors) and the collection point (Gateways) secure?
- Are data communications connections between the collection point (Gateway) and the data storage point (Cloud) secure?
- Explain any additional Security concerns or issues relating to the ID and OI used to construct the Target Outcome Current Value.

Data Analysis Levels

The data you create from your IoT deployment is the cornerstone of realizing a successful IoT Target Outcome. The following diagram shows 6 levels of Operational Intelligence.

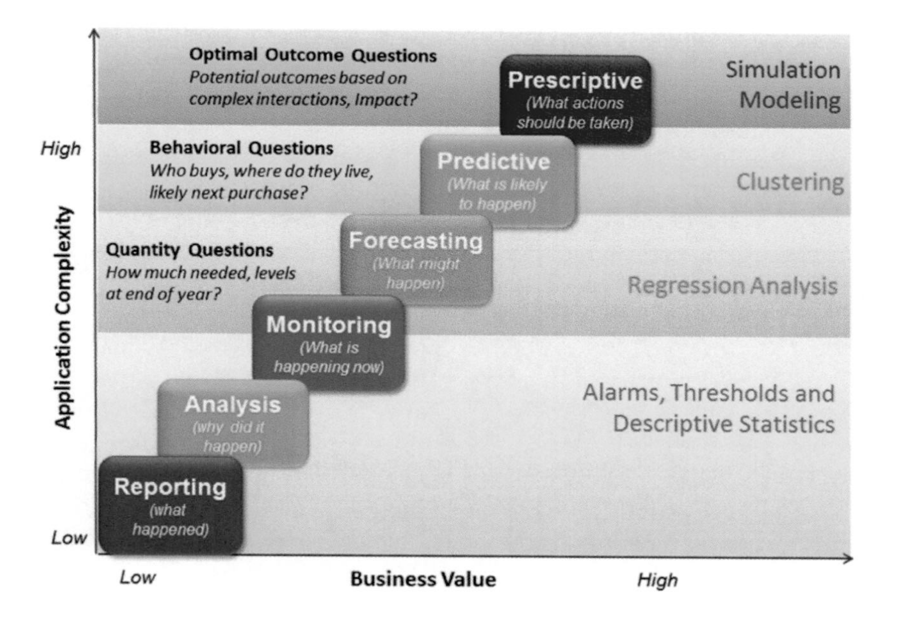

This diagram maps Application Complexity from low to high on the Y axis and Business Value from low to high on the X axis. You will use database technologies and analysis software applications to transform your IoT Infrastructure Data into real-time Operational Intelligence. You can see the correlation between Application Complexity and Business

Value which is not surprising. The more intelligence and automation you build into your IoT Data Analysis tools, your results will be more advanced and actionable. In the case of Prescriptive analysis, the results may drive automation that controls physical infrastructure autonomously. Also, other Enterprise software systems can be automatically updated with IoT data results that drive actions in those systems.

In order of increasing sophistication:

1. **Reporting** - what happened – IoT data is collected and stored for review at a future point in time. This data might be: monitored parameters sent at prescribed intervals, threshold crossings, or inactivity indicators. This type of data is usually presented in a chronological data report, or filtered by some user selectable criteria.
2. **Analysis** – why did it happen – Stored IoT data is now subjected to analysis algorithms that look for cause and effect mechanisms across the IoT data set.
3. **Monitoring** – what's happening now – At this level, real-time elements are utilized that dramatically impact the configuration and capabilities of your IoT deployment. Alarms, threshold crossings, alerts and other time-critical IoT data is received, analyzed and notifications are sent. The urgency of these monitoring transactions demand low latency which affects your entire IoT Deployment. Sensor reactions to monitored conditions will happen immediately and reported. Gateways will forward this information immediately to the IoT Services Software Platform that is programmed to analyze data automatically and take action extremely quickly. People and systems receive alerts through various mechanisms. These real-time IoT data analysis capabilities will increase the cost and complexity of your IoT deployment due to data latency requirements.
4. **Forecasting** - what might happen - using data collected over time, trends can be calculated using regression analysis and other data tools. Often forecasting business intelligence deals with quantities. How much as been used? How much is needed to optimize the process?
5. **Predictive** – what is likely to happen - this data analysis is fairly sophisticated using techniques such as cluster analysis. Stored IoT data is passed through sophisticated data analysis tools such as clustering.

6. **Prescriptive** – what actions should be taken - This is the top of the data analysis complexity spectrum. Sophisticated analysis tools utilize data and trend analysis to prescribe actions be taken automatically or instructions to be passed to human operators.

The intelligence to be applied to the data is defined in your IoT Data Baselining project. The software tools are created or purchased in your IoTblueprint phase and then installed and tested in the IoTdeploy phase.

Baseline Engineering and Support Resources

Now we turn to the "people-side" by identifying design engineering resources for hardware, software, database design, network design, implementation, and maintenance. Baseline areas include:

- How will the IoT sensors, network, cloud and software be installed and tested end-to-end?
- How will the IoT installations be supported and maintained ?

Required Areas of IoT Expertise

Determination of staff skills follows the IoT implantation process steps:

- Make or Buy Sensors
- Embedded software required for Sensors and/or Gateways
- Wireless Protocols for Enterprise and M2M
- Security on devices, network, cloud, applications and users
- Software Applications on Cloud or Private
- Platform as a Service Data Analytics

You need to identify the IoT Development Skills and Resources that will be responsible for your IoT deployment.

- Does your Organization have Program Management to complete complex end-to-end Hardware/Software & System development?
- Does your Organization have Wireless Sensor Networking Protocol Experience?
- Do you have a H/W Development Group - with EC, RF, Sensor & uC Experience?
- Do you have Embedded Systems Programming Experience?

- Do you have programmers to Develop Code to implement Sense & Control Algorithms?
- Do you have programmers to Develop Middle-ware between Sensor Arrays & Cloud?
- Do you have a support organization to implement sensor data transport to Cloud, analytics, BI extraction and delivery to users, clients & control systems?
- Do you have programmers to Developing End-to-End Secure data communications (Sensor to Cloud to User/Application)?
- Do you have programmers to Develop Analytics for Data Visualization & Business Intelligence (BI)?
- Do you have programmers to Create Apps that present BI to Users in a way that it is actionable & usable to enable Business Processes to be Optimized?
- Do you have programmers to write Applications to distribute BI to Users, Processes & Machines?
- Is there experience in outsourcing, contracting & managing 3rd party developers on complex projects?
- Do you have in-House End System Certification for CE, FCC, UL, etc…

Once you have answered these questions, group your answers into these 3 categories to be able to assess the level of your current IoT resources and skills:

1. IoT Skills and Disciplines that are lacking in your Organization
2. IoT Skills and Disciplines that need improvement in your Organization
3. IoT Skills and disciplines that are strengths in your Organization

You will be able to construct a Capabilities Summary like this table from the IoTaudit System report document.

IoT Skills & Disciplines that are lacking in Organization:

- Wireless Sensor Networking
- MiddleWare from Sensor to Cloud Development
- Capability to Support End to End Sensors to BI Implementation
- End to End (Sensors to BI) Security
- Analytics for Data Visualization & Business Intelligence
- Business Intelligence Application Development
- Application Development to distribute BI to Users, Processes & Machines

IoT Skills & Disciplines that will need improvement in Organization:

- Hardware Sensor Design
- Embedded Systems Programming
- Sense & Control Algorithm Development

IoT Skills & Disciplines that are strengths in Organization:

- Program Management
- Outsourcing Complex Projects to 3rd Parties
- System Certification for UL, CE, FCC, etc.

After reviewing your staffing assessment, your team can determine the best way forward on your IoT project – outsource, partner, hire staff, or internal development with current staff.

IoT Project Financial Considerations

Your next Baseline task is to determine and document the current financial issues surrounding your IoT Project.

- How does your current corporate Project methodology impact your IoT Target Data. What are the financial implications?
- How will your team forecast and track the IoT Project Expenses?
- How will you forecast hardware, network, cloud and software maintenance costs?

- What methods will be used to forecast hardware replacement life expectations and replacement costs?
- How will you forecast and track software support costs and upgrade charges over IoT deployment lifetime?

Combine Baseline and Backtrack Techniques

It is very difficult to start from your Current status and identify all the actions required to realize your Target Outcome. There are many areas and issues where you will not have insights. Using the Backtracking process you begin by starting with your Target Value and brainstorm backwards to your Current Value using "Why-How-What" questioning techniques. This process looks like this diagram:

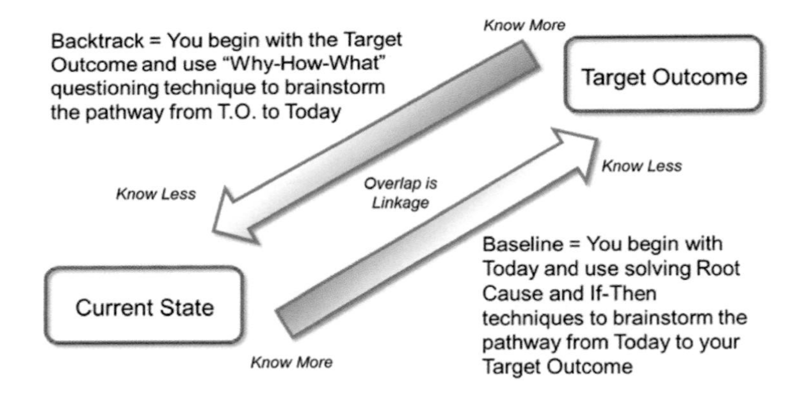

The shaded arrows show the information confidence you have starting from both directions – dark is more and white is less. Notice if you use Baselining and Backtracking from both sides, you can merge your information into a comprehensive Baseline database that will be used to create a robust StratGraph. Note: you will often find that the two paths do not intersect. These areas of ambiguity often turn out to be risk areas that need to be examined further before you start on your IoT deployment.

Using Baseline/Backtrack Data for Your IoT Strategy

The Baseline process is incredibly important to your IoT planning as it is the foundation of your Strategy! Done correctly, the Baseline exercise identifies the process and steps you will need to take you from today to a successful IoT Target Outcome tomorrow.

Expectations for IoT

More Projects Fail Because of People...

In the Baseline process we collected information on many aspects and issues of your IoT implementation. In the Expectations process we will investigate and document all your IoT people and resource issues. You will be conducting interviews with all your various IoT stakeholders – IoT Coalition team, Senior leaders, Affected internal organizations, Customers, Supply chain, Investor responses, and Competitive responses. The BEST System places particular emphasis on the Expectations process because it is often one of the most difficult hurdles to achieving your IoT Target Outcome. Unidentified expectations and misassumptions is often the root cause of IoT Project failure.

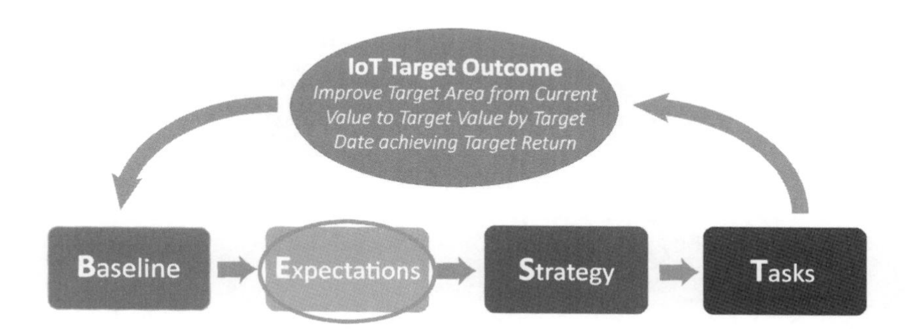

Why are Expectations Important?

Your IoT business transformation success depends on the ability of the people in your organization to effectively change the way they do business. Every person holds a set of current expectations concerning many things both professional and personal.

The definition of expectation is: to look forward to, regard as likely to happen, anticipate the occurrence of, a strong belief that something will happen in the future, or a belief that someone will or should achieve something. Expect is a verb that is alway used with an object. "I expect ___(fill in the blank)". So Expectations have clearly defined outcomes. They can be very directive - "I expect this task to be done tomorrow" , or aspirational - "I expect to achieve my IoT Target Outcome."

It is very important to note these key definition words: look forward to, likely to happen, anticipate, belief, will/should achieve all express a sense of faith and hope. Belief is a state or habit of mind in which trust or confidence is placed in some person or thing. Faith is confidence or trust in a person or thing; or a belief not based on proof. Hope is a feeling of desire for a certain thing to happen. These are all emotions combined knowledge gained to date. Expectations are not always logical and they re often misinformed.

It's no wonder then when your IoT Coalition team sits down to discuss your IoT project everyone comes to the table with different expectations. The BEST System Expectations process is used to uncover, discuss, and negotiate all your IoT Stakeholders' individual expectations into a set of shared expectations.

Winners make a habit of manufacturing their own positive expectations in advance of the event.

Brian Tracy

Which IoT Stakeholders' Expectations are Important?

You must be able to identify all the stakeholders in your IOT Target Outcome. There are two tiers of stakeholders. The Tier 1 stakeholders are your IoT Coalition who directly influence your Target Outcome. They are also the people are often most affected by your journey and attainment of your TO. The Tier 2 stakeholders do not directly influence your Target Outcome but they will be affected by your IoT Target Outcome and do influence your Tier 1 stakeholders.

You need to use a structured approach for IoT Expectations assessment. These are the steps that are embodied in the IoTaudit System:

1. Identify all the Tier 1 and Tier 2 IoT stakeholders to be interviewed
    - Target Outcome Owner
    - Sponsoring Executive (if different than TO owner)

- Project Leader
- Project Team Members – The "Key Believers" who make it happen
- Extended Team – staff and organizations supporting the IoT project
- Internal Detractors – those negatively affected by IoT project
- Senior Executives – Dictating strategy and corporate objectives
- Shareholders/Investors – private or public. Board of Directors
- Customers – Understand positive and negative impacts

2. Collect and Document Expectations from all involved parties
   - Remember everyone has different agendas and goals.
   - Several may not match with your IoT Target Outcome
3. Understand Synergies and Conflicts across all stakeholders
4. Identify those responsible for IoT Project funding
5. Identify Staffing Resource requirements – Skills and numbers
6. Understand timeline from perspective of project team vs Management
7. Competitors – Current initiatives, reaction to your IoT project
8. Stakeholder Investment expectations How much will the IoT project cost?
9. Stakeholder Timelines – when will project start, finish, delay impacts?
10. Identify "Who did I miss?" and "Who comes in later?"

Creating your IoT Stakeholder Heat Map

Identify the Lead Stakeholder in every department that will be affected by your IoT deployment and ask them the following questions and document their answers to use as rating information:

1. Do you agree with the IoT Target Outcome?
2. Is there a Positive or Negative impact to you from IoT?

3. How important is achieving IoT success?
4. Will you commit the resources required for IoT success?

Depending on the responses from each individual, you place them on a grid showing their showing their support for your IoT Project vs. the impact the IoT Project will have on their area. Your IoT Stakeholder Heat Map will look something like this: You can see from this example from an IoTaudit used with a Smart Connected Product Vendor, there are currently several IoT Stakeholders in the Green quadrant. These stakeholders support the IoT Project and are positively impacted by the IoT Target Outcome.

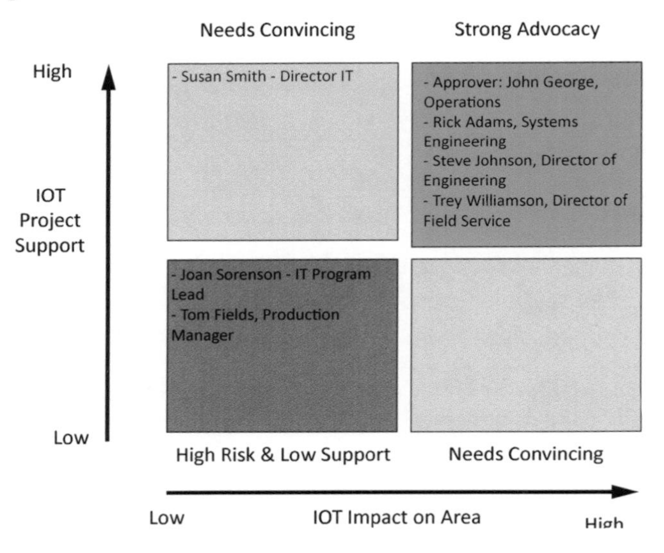

However, IoT Stakeholders in the Red area are a source of grave concern. These individuals have low support for the IoT Project. This is due to either they do not agree with the IoT Project and/or the IoT Project has little or negative effect on their area or organization. Discussions must be held with this negative IoT Stakeholders get them engaged and enlisted. At a minimum these individuals need to be moved into Yellow areas of support.

People are a Key Cause of IoT Project Failure

The Calleam "Wheel of Failure" was created from interviews with 300 companies and highlights 8 classes of Project Failure. A majority of the failures were People-related - Organizational, Leadership, Teamwork, Leadership, Underestimation, Skills, and Competency.

Expectations and Conflict

Conflict is created when the expectations of two more parties are different. Conflict is resolved by compromise when parties agree to set aside less important parts of their expectations to obtain more important expectations. So the prioritization of Expectations is critical. What are you willing to do or not do to achieve your IoT Target Outcome?

Identifying stakeholder expectations is why you assemble your IoT Coalition to supply multiple perspectives. You must have a clear understanding of the ramifications of meeting or not meeting your IoT Stakeholders expectations. What are: "must haves", "nice to haves" and "non-negotiables"?

Expectations and Trust

Trust is created when Expectations are met. You trust others when they meet your expectations. Other people trust you when you meet their expectations. Therefore, the only way trust can be created is by very clearly understanding expectations. You must clearly explain your expectations to others and you must draw out clear expectations from them. People are not good at expressing their expectations on their own– they feel it is self-centered, boastful or at least intrusive on others. Therefore, you must be the one to ask – empower other people to tell you their expectations – make it allowed, make it safe, make it a two way street. Once someone gives you their expectations, it is easy for you to reciprocate and tell them your expectations. Fair is fair after all.

Understanding Expectations – the 4 E's

All your IoT project stakeholders need to go through the engage, educate, empathy and enlist process. You are going to ask open-ended and cause & effect questions about the proposed IoT project. You will then LISTEN and document their answers. Be sensitive to everyone's responses as:

The most important thing in communication is hearing what isn't said.

Peter Drucker

Using the 4E's process you are going to identify who is positively and negatively impacted by the IoT Project. You will determine how to educate all your stakeholders by addressing their hot buttons and issues. Lastly, you need to get all stakeholders enlisted in your IoT Success. Diagramming the 4E's looks like this:

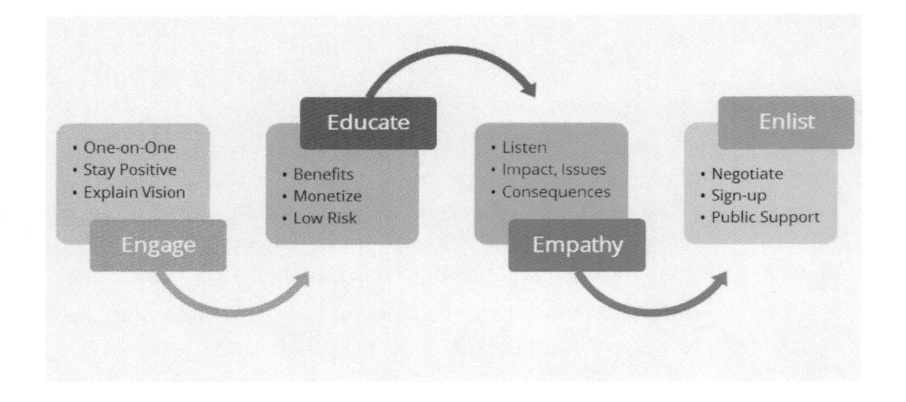

These are the steps:

1. **Engage** – You begin with a one-on-one meeting in a comfortable setting. Using a positive attitude you start with your IoT Target Outcome. You describe the vivid vision that has been developed so far and how you see them playing a role in the Target Outcome success.
2. **Educate** – You make sure the other person understands "what's in it for them" You explain the benefits of the Target Outcome in terms how the Target Outcome will: Save them money, Make them money or Provide a new opportunity. Then for each of these you will describe How Much, How Soon and How Sure

3. **Empathy**- You will listen, fully explore and understand the other persons, attitudes, feelings, issues and options. This is accomplished by using open ended questions such as: "How does this impact you?" "How does this impact your organization?", "Describe the positive outcomes", "Describe the undesired consequences", "Who else do you think is affected by the IoT Target Outcome?". The answer to the last question often leads to adding unknown IoT Stakeholders.
4. **Enlist** – Your goal of this conversation is to understand the other person's expectations, negotiate differences, and create a set of shared expectations that drive IoT Business Transformation success. It is critical to have them sign-up in writing. After getting shared expectations documented, you must continually check-in with your IoT Stakeholders to make sure they continue to support your IoT Project. Things change - don't be surprised!

I cannot over-emphasize the importance of using the 4E's process with your IoT stakeholders. It takes a committed team with various skills to produce a successful IoT deployment.

Get it in Writing

Now that you have had a two-way discussion on Expectations – you need to concretely agree on each party's understanding. This is best documented in writing. There is a visceral feeling of commitment when you write down your expectations. More importantly, your discussion and agreed upon shared expectation will be documented. This agreement can take various forms of formality depending on: Do you need a written trail? Are there legally binding terms? Does the agreement have financial terms and implications? Here are some documentation types:

- Email Agreement - both parties should write down their expectations and send to the other party. The receiving party should send an acknowledge email that indicates agreement or disagreement if that still exists.
- Memorandum of Understanding - this may be more appropriate with an IoT Stakeholder who is not a member of your organization.
- Written Legal Contract - this is often required with your IoT suppliers - hardware, software, and/or services.

Documenting the expectations of your IoT Stakeholders takes time. But your time is well rewarded when down the road people "forget" what they committed and you can "remind" them. Believe in the saying:

"Get it in Writing to avoid the Fighting!"

Steve Grady

Tackle Strategy Next

With your IoT Target Outcome, Baseline and Expectations analyses complete, you are prepared to construct your IoT Strategy and StratGraph.

Strategy for Your IoT Deployment

Victorious warriors win first and then go to war...

At this point, you have done three critical steps that many organizations fail to do well in their IoT planning: Create an IoT Target Outcome, Baseline the situation, and articulate the Expectations of all your IoT Target Object stakeholders. You now have enough data to create your IoT Strategy which is the means to achieve your IoT Target Outcome end. Recall this diagram used earlier to discuss your Target Outcome Purpose. Now we focus on your Strategy creation process.

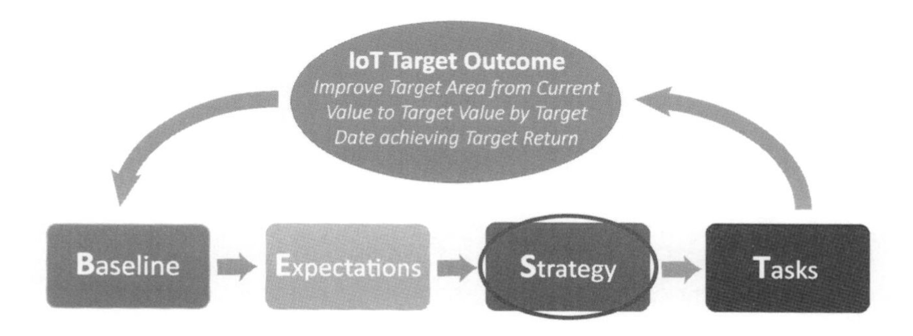

What is Strategy?

After years of research, I have found this is the best definition of Strategy:

Strategy is a coherent coordination of policies and actions designed to achieve a high-stakes challenge.

Take a minute before you move on. How does this Strategy definition jive with what your organization calls Strategy? We are going to use this definition as a baseline for the rest of this Strategy chapter.

There are many key words in this Strategy definition:

1. **Coherent** - your strategic plans need to be logical, consistent and orderly.
2. **Coordination** - there needs to be linkages between all the elements of your strategy.
3. **Policies** - you will have precise and rigorous procedures and guidelines that all IoT project team members will utilize.
4. **Actions** - a person is directly accountable for the tasks to get an assignment completed.
5. **Designed** - Strategy is created and executed with a structured process that is visualized as a graph.
6. **Achieve** - your Strategy is designed to produce a successful outcome. Everyone on your IoT project team must believe in your Strategy.
7. **High-Stakes** - your strategy is centered on your IoT Target Outcome Area which is vitally important to your organization.
8. **Challenge** - this suggests your IoT Target Outcome will not be easy, but extremely rewarding when achieved.

How to Document and Visualize Strategy

Creating, documenting and visualizing strategy is a difficult process and has been the topic of academic and business discussions for decades. There are several excellent resources on Strategy including the books by Robert Kaplan and David Norton: Balanced Scorecard, Strategy Maps, and The Strategy-Focused Organization. Their approach is best suited for high level corporate strategy and is based on a four tier model of Customer, Financial, Internal Processes, and Learning & Growth.

The Balanced Scorecard/Strategy Map approach is a great start, but there are several inherent flaws in light of our definition of Strategy. It's that there is no clear process for coordinating actions. When you look at a Kaplan/Norton style Strategy Map there are a set of bubbles in layers with lots of arrows pointing every which way. Unfortunately, Team members have no sense of priority or direction - it is simply not effective for taking coherent action.

Understandably it is really is hard to visualize a coherent coordinated Strategy Map. Just Google "Strategy Maps" and see what you find:

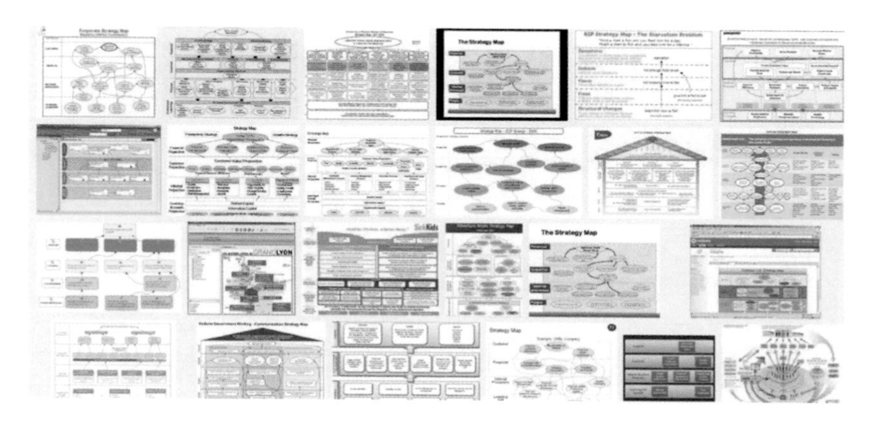

I realize the diagrams are too small to decipher, but is does not improve at all at life-size! How on earth is your IoT Coalition supposed to achieve your IoT Target Outcome using these visualizations of strategy? Here is a strategy diagram from the screen shot above which is for a Boys and Girls Club. I feel like I just got off the Tilt-a-Whirl at the State Fair!

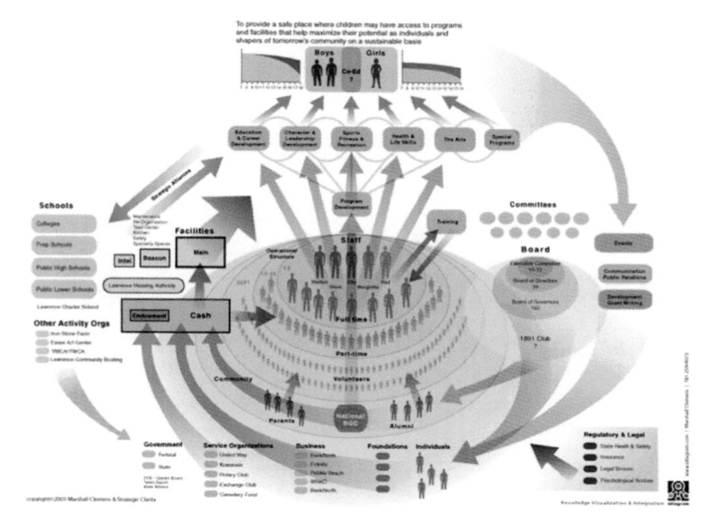

So we need way to visualize strategy the incorporates all the tenets of the strategy definition, but can actually be used by your IoT Coalition.

Introducing the StratGraph

A new way to visualize Strategy is the BEST System StratGraph. A StratGraph chart shows all the elements of the Strategic process combined with concepts of Coordination, Action and Target Outcome achievement. We will use the StratGraph approach to build your IoT Strategy.

The overall format of the StratGraph shown below has 5 components:

A - Strategy Data Collection

B - Strategy Focus Areas

C - Strategy Realization Process

D - Coherent Coordinated Strategic Action Areas

E - IoT Business Transformation Target Outcome

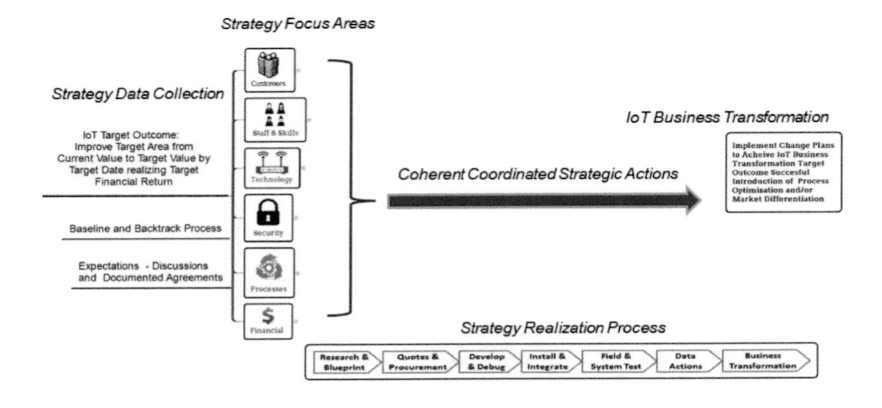

Let's detail each of these 5 StratGraph components:

A - Strategy Data Collection

The work you accomplished in the first three steps of the BEST System provides the foundational input data to construct your IoT StratGraph that achieves your Target Outcome IoT business transformation.

- IoT Target Outcome and Vision Document
- Baseline & Backtrack information
- Expectations with negotiated agreements

B - Strategy Focus Areas

This portion of the IoT StratGraph identifies your fundamental IoT Strategy Focus Areas. The analysis work you did in Baseline and Expectations provides the background information for each area:

- Customers - Internal and External
- Staff and Skills - Culture, Competencies, Resources
- Technology - IoT, Legacy infrastructure, Data
- Security - Data, Communications, Physical sites
- Processes - Target Area, Current, New, Transformation
- Financial - Return, Costs, Risks, Business Model, Competitors

Each of the Strategy Focus Areas will have a different member of the IoT Coalition assigned to lead and manage this Strategy Stream. For almost all organizations this implies that there are a minimum 7 members in an IoT Coalition team.

C - Strategy Realization Process

This portion of the IoT StratGraph provides the process to drive actions in the quest to achieve your Target Outcome. In the IoT StratGraph diagram, the "X-axis" is 7 IoT project phases starting from the Research/ Blueprint Phase and ending with the Business Transformation phase. The Strategy Realization Process provides the Strategy Flow for creating, coordinating and assigning your Strategic Action Areas.

D - Strategic Action Areas

Now we can begin to identify and document the Strategic Action Areas that will be the foundational template for our IoT Tasks Implementation Plan. Strategic Action Areas are "Super-Tasks" that will be broken down into appropriate Tasks. The simplified IoT StratGraph diagram has a large arrow representing the collection of many Strategic Action Areas. An actual IoT StratGraph has all the Strategic Action Areas described coherently and coordinated to drive IoT Business Transformation success.

E - IoT Business Transformation

The final component of the IoT StratGraph is your IoT Target Outcome and Business Transformation results. Recall purpose of Strategy is to "... achieve a high-stakes Challenge". Therefore, it is vital that any StratGraph end with achieving at your IoT Business Transformation success.

IoT StratGraph Full Expanded View

This StratGraph diagram below shows the details of the Strategic Action Areas and their relationships between other Strategic Focus Areas. This diagram does have the visual flavor of a PERT chart given the flow, arrows and Strategy Realization Process.

All the Strategic Areas are converge to the IoT Target Outcome. I realize this IoT StratGraph is impossible to read in this book and can be viewed here: www.enviro-controls.com/iottransform.

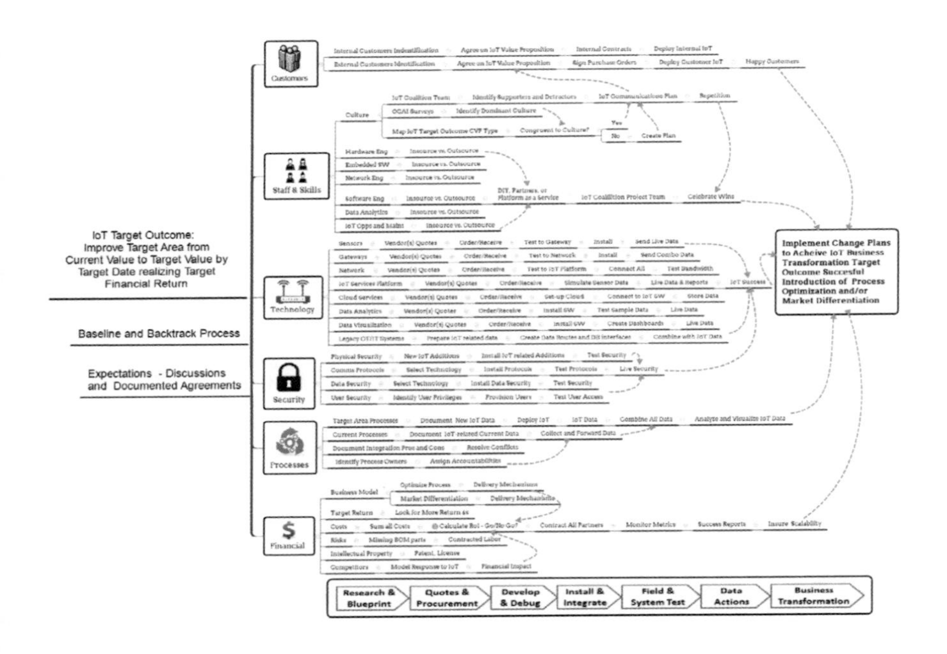

StratGraph - "What We Will Do and Will Not Do"

Your IoT StratGraph documents the Strategic Actions you will execute to realize your Target Outcome. But as strategy guru Michael Porter stated,

"The essence of Strategy is choosing what not to do."

Michael Porter

There are always trade-offs caused by limitations of technology, time, money and personnel. When constructing your StratGraph, include the key elements of success and nothing more. The coherency of your StratGraph depends on this. You must effectively communicate this to all your IoT Stakeholders: "If something is not on the StratGraph, it means we are truly not going to do it. "

Tools for Building an IoT StratGraph

The IoT StratGraphs shown in this book and incorporated into the IoTaudit System utilize a "mind map format". The tool that created this StratGraph and the other mind maps in this book is Xmind - www.xmind.net. You can try this tool for free. To receive an Xmind template for the IoT StratGraph go here: www.enviro-controls.com/iottransform.

IoT StratGraph Use Guidelines

In order to execute your StratGraph successfully, you must follow these key guidelines:

1. **Your IoT StratGraph is a living document.** This is not one of those big 3 ring binder corporate Strategy Plans that sits on the shelf collecting dust. The IoT StratGraph Strategic Action Areas are meant to be updated as you move through the IoT business transformation process. As your IoT project progresses, you will learn new things and hit roadblocks What you will not change is your IoT Target Outcome. This wise saying from 2500 years ago still applies:

"When it is obvious that the goal cannot be reached, don't adjust the goal, adjust the action steps."

Confucius

2. **Communicate, Communicate, Communicate** - It is absolutely vital that all your IoT Stakeholders see and understand your IoT StratGraph. All your IoT Stakeholders need to understand your strategy - employees, suppliers, partners, and customers - as that is the only way they can buy-in. As we will discuss in the IoTtransform chapter, you must attempt to over-communicate your IoT Target Outcome and Plans. Your Leaders must be very vocal.

3. **Negotiate Accountabilities** - every Strategic Focus Area or Strategic Acton Area will have a single accountable person assigned. No Groups, Departments, etc. - It must be a person who has agreed to accept the assignment. Your IoT

Coalition has to use the IoT StratGraph every day – it is not left to an elite group in an ivory tower.

4. **Execution is the final element of Strategy**. The whole purpose of creating your IoT StratGraph is to achieve your IoT Target Outcome. Therefore, the IoT Coalition Team members need to lead their IoT Project support teams into action using your IoT StratGraph as the rallying tool.

Moving to Your IoT Implementation Tasks Plan

Having completed the first version of your StratGraph, we will now build your detailed IoT Implementation Tasks Plan which will provide the actionable details for each of your Strategic Action Areas.

TASKs Plan for your IoT Implementation

Vision Without Action is Merely a Dream...

With your StratGraph completed, you are now ready to build your IoT Implementation Tasks Plan that will drive a successful Target Outcome.

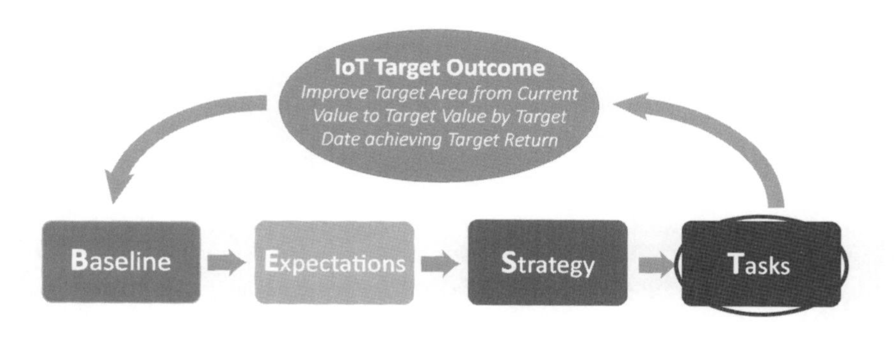

The word for the final phase of the BEST System - TASKs - was chosen very specifically. TASK is an amalgam of 4 areas which comprise the TASK acronym:

T – Time – A Task has a specific start date and finish date assigned to it when the desired output of this task is to be realized.

A - Accountability – a single person is accountable to get this Task done. It sometimes may be you. But most often it is another person, and the IoT Project Manager must discuss and agree on the shared Expectations of the output of this task.

S – Steps – these are the specific actions that must be taken to achieve the task. It is very useful to break these down. If there are a lot of steps in a task output, you may want to break down this larger task into smaller tasks.

K – Keep Score – Create and use the IoT tasks project schedule that identifies all steps to be done by who by when. Create and use an IoT KPI Scorecard. Measure Team engagement by survey (in person or third party)

Time

Every task has a start date and a finish date to be documented in your project plan. Time is one of the most important components of urgency. Urgency is an absolute requirement for IoT business transformation. There is an overall urgency to your project described in your IoT Target Outcome as your Target Date. But obviously, all the tasks that lead up to your Target Date need to be accomplished on time in order to successfully accomplish your Target Outcome.

"The bad news is time flies. The good news is you're the pilot"

Michael Altshule

Accountability

Each of your tasks need to have a single person accountable for accomplishing the task. Accountabilities do not reside with groups or teams; they point to a single name. This goes back to the old saying "I'd like to have one hand to shake or one neck to ring". Now accountability in the BEST System is to be used only in the positive sense. Many organizations use accountability in a negative fashion - that "one neck to ring". Rather in a culture of positive accountability, team members volunteer and own their tasks. Their leadership team gives them the tools and are empowered to be successful. Many studies have shown that a companies with a culture high in positive accountability are often very successful both with their customers and in their financial results.

The Importance of Accountability in Business Transformation

Accountability is one of the linchpins of a successful IOT business transformation. In their book "Change the Culture, Change the Game" by Roger Connors and Tom Smith, the authors show that creating accountability for results energizes your organization and drives breakthrough strategy. They remind us that accountability in many organizations is something that happens to you when things go wrong. And if this is the case in your organization, your leaders must be committed to reverse this course of behavior. Using accountability with a positive capital A, staff at every level in an organization can understand and embrace their role in facilitating change.

Leaders who are going to lead an effective IOT business transformation will promote and demand accountability in their organization. But this will be the good kind of accountability - where those who step up and accept responsibility for change are provided the tools they need to succeed. Should team members struggle in their task, it is a failure of the organization to properly assign and/or support accountability. In highly accountable organizations failure seen as learning, and learnings should happen as quickly as possible. Note that accountability is in the TASKs part of the BEST System. We are in IoT Implementation phase where many things need to happen simultaneously. We are in the "Do" phase of the Plan/Do/Check/Anchor process.

Accountability when understood and applied correctly, will improve an organization's result in dramatic ways. The BEST System provides everyone in the organization with an understanding of where we are, where we want to go, what people expect, the strategy for accomplishing the Target Outcome, and documentation of everyone's accountabilities in the IoT Project plan.

Steps

You will break down your StratGraph Strategic Actions into atomic subtasks and actions that must be completed in order to realize your IoT Target Outcome. Each step and action will be documented in your IoT Project Planning Tool with specific dependencies, outputs and due dates.

Keep Score

It is vital to know the status and progress of your IoT project at all times. Closely monitoring your progress helps identify urgent issues that need to be addressed. Also, you're able to share success with your IoT Coalition Team and your IoT stakeholders. The ability to celebrate small wins along the road of your IoT project is a key driver to implement the changes in your organization that will support your IoT business transformation. In the chapter on Tasks Plan, we will discuss new on-line collaboration and tracking tools that will accelerate your time to IoT success.

IoT Implementation Plan Success Criteria

A successful IoT Implementation Plan depends on successful utilization of the "4A's":

- Assumptions – must resolve them to facts
- Alignments – Expectations must be aligned across all IoT Project Team members
- Accountabilities – identify the individuals who will own each Task/Step
- Agreements – all IoT Project Team members must commit to realizing a successful IoT business transformation.

IoT Project Scope and Scale Levels

In order to reduce IoT Project risks, it is prudent to consider scaling your IoT deployment by starting small then growing to your full IoT implementation.

- IoT Proof of Concept – smart with a small amount of connected devices, simple connectivity and limited software complexity. Collect and readout specific device data. Identify the IoT processes and rules along with potential scaling issues
- Sophisticated Single Domain IoT – drive up the scale to hundreds/thousands of connected devices, more communication and significant data storage/analysis
- Multi-Domain IoT – providing IoT services across a range of Business functions leveraging a common architecture, communication network and application software deployments.

Turning Your IoT StratGraph into IoT TASKs Plan

You will now create your IoT Implementation TASKs plan in your organization's standard Project Management software tools.

Recall the key precepts of Strategy - Coherency, Coordination and Challenge There are some excellent on-line Project Management tools that can be used to simplify and streamline your IoT TASKs plan data input and radically improve your IoT Team collaboration. These include:

SmartSheet - This online tool is like Microsoft Excel on steroids is used by hundreds of thousands of companies. The IoT Project Plan you create in SmartSheet is shared amongst your entire IoT Coalition. Your plan becomes completely interactive with prompts for upcoming tasks, task completion alerts and exception reporting. SmartSheet has several useful views and Dashboards of your IoT Project. This is the tool Enviro-Controls uses to manage our IoT Smart Overlay Platform as a Service projects. You can get more information here: www.enviro-controls.com/iottransform.

Slack - Millions of users have adopted Slack as their organizations collaboration tool. It is a mash-up of project management and chat. You would set-up channels for each of your Strategic Focus Areas and assign members to each who can share files and real-time message each other. Many companies have done away with email for anything project related. You would still need to create your IoT Project Plan in a tool like Microsoft Project or SmartSheet.

Wrike - This on-line tool suite was built for Project Managers and is essentially a combination of Microsoft Project, Smart Sheet and Slack to provide Project Management tools with collaboration methods. Wrike utilizes real-time reporting, analytics, dashboards and email integrations to help manage IoT Plan activities. More information is here: www.enviro-controls.com/iottransform.

Once you have selected your IoT Project Plan tool, here are the steps to create your IoT TASKs Plan from your IoT StratGraph.

A. Use the IoT StratGraph Strategy Realization Process Phases

Your IoT TASKs plan timeline should utilize the Strategy Realization Process steps. Your tasks will be in one of these phases:

1. Research
2. Blueprint
3. Procurement
4. Develop and Debug
5. Install and Integrate
6. Field and System Test
7. Data Analysis Actions
8. Business Transformation Actions

B. Use Your IoT StratGraph Strategic Focus Areas

With your IoT Project Timeline Phases laid out, you utilize your Strategic Focus Area as the major Task categories. List each of your Strategic Actions as a separate major Task. Then begin the detailed breakdown into sub-tasks, steps, and actions. Each of these elements will have: description of deliverable, a start date, an end date, a single person assigned, input dependencies and output dependencies.

C. Breakdown Your IoT StratGraph Strategic Actions

You will now create subtasks and steps for each of your Strategic Actions. These subtasks/steps will be assigned to a single person, with start date, end date, and incoming/outgoing dependencies at a minimum.

D. Create your Detailed IoT Project Plan

Have each of your Strategic Focus Area owners do a work breakdown of their area creating the subtasks and steps. For each subtask in their area, they will be responsible for: describing the requirements and deliverables, identifying the accountable owner, defining the start and finish dates, identifying input and output dependencies, identifying the resources (money, skills, tools, etc.) needed and planning contingency paths if encountered.

Now enter all the IoT Project data into your tracking tool. An example IoT TASKs Plan would look like:

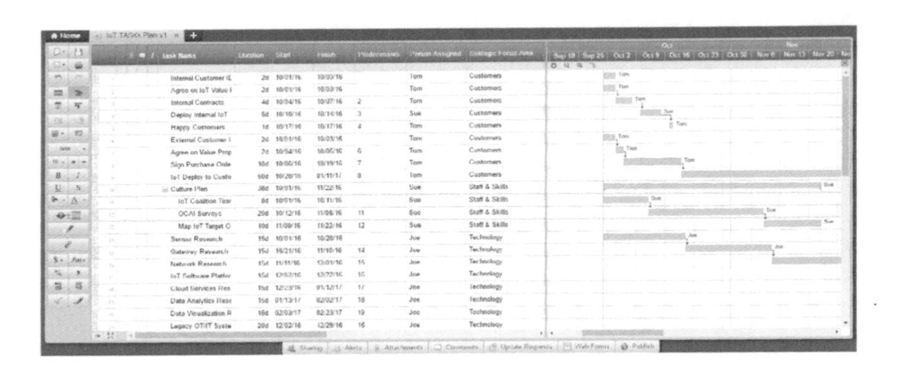

Task Name	Duration	Start	Finish	Predecessors	Person Assigned	Strategic Focus Area
Internal Customer IL	2d	10/01/16	10/03/16		Tom	Customers
Agree on IoT Value I	2d	10/01/16	10/03/16		Tom	Customers
Internal Contracts	4d	10/04/16	10/07/16	2	Tom	Customers
Deploy Internal IoT	5d	10/10/16	10/14/16	3	Sue	Customers
Happy Customers	1d	10/17/16	10/17/16	4	Tom	Customers
External Customer I	2d	10/01/16	10/03/16		Tom	Customers
Agree on Value Prop	2d	10/04/16	10/05/16	6	Tom	Customers
Sign Purchase Orde	10d	10/06/16	10/19/16	7	Tom	Customers
IoT Deploy to Custo	60d	10/20/16	01/11/17	8	Tom	Customers
Culture Plan	38d	10/01/16	11/22/16		Sue	Staff & Skills
IoT Coalition Tear	8d	10/01/16	10/11/16		Sue	Staff & Skills
OCAI Surveys	20d	10/12/16	11/08/16	11	Sue	Staff & Skills
Map IoT Target O	10d	11/09/16	11/22/16	12	Sue	Staff & Skills
Sensor Research	15d	10/01/16	10/20/16		Joe	Technology
Gateway Research	15d	10/21/16	11/10/16	14	Joe	Technology
Network Research	15d	11/11/16	12/01/16	15	Joe	Technology
IoT Software Platfor	15d	12/02/16	12/22/16	16	Joe	Technology
Cloud Services Res	15d	12/23/16	01/12/17	17	Joe	Technology
Data Analytics Rese	15d	01/13/17	02/02/17	18	Joe	Technology
Data Visualization R	16d	02/03/17	02/23/17	19	Joe	Technology
Legacy OT/IT Syste	20d	12/02/16	12/29/16	16	Joe	Technology

The details are hard to read at this size, but you can see the structure of Task data and Gantt Chart showing the timeline and dependencies. Using the Gantt Chart view of the data you can identify your IoT Project Critical path which is vital to understanding the key tasks that drive your schedule.

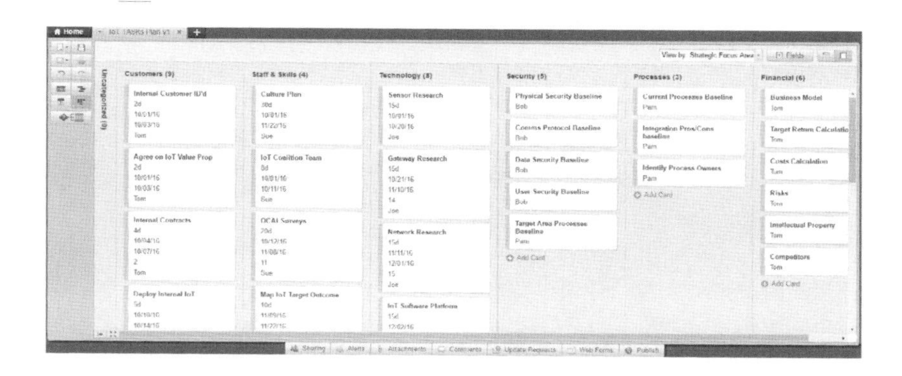

Each of your Strategic Focus areas will have an IoT Coalition team member assigned and accountable for the tasks in this area. This is an efficient way to have team members report their status.

Another useful dashboard view of your IoT Project Data is by the IoT Process phases in order of Timeline. The Research phase is on the left and the Transform phase is on the far right. Of course this view will change throughout the lifecycle of your IoT Project as Tasks are completed in each phase.

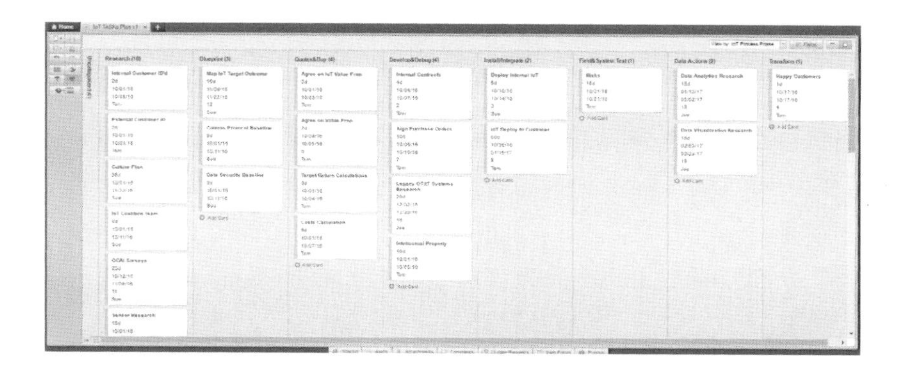

Review all 3 IoT Project charts in full size detail at: www.enviro-controls.com/iottransform. You now have the process and tools to build your IoT TASKs Plan.   As expressed in the words of the one of the greats in Project Management:

"Plans are only good intentions unless they immediately degenerate into hard work."

Peter Drucker

IoT Risk Management

Never Let Anyone Say"I Told You So"...

Throughout your entire Internet of Things journey you must utilize tools and process that reduce the risk of failure at each stage of your project. The IoT Business Transformation System provides the following tools that reduce risk at each stage of your IoT process:

1. **IoTaudit** - This is the most important process for de-risking your IoT deployment. Your team will create and communicate your IoT Target outcome which puts all your IoT Stakeholders on the same page. Then you go through the IoTaudit processes: Baseline, Expectations, Strategy and Tasks.
2. **Premortem Workshop** – Using this process, your team go through all the ways your project could fail versus waiting to the end of the project with the incriminating "I told you so's". Identifying all the failure mechanisms up front and creating contingencies de-risks your IoT StratGraph and Tasks Plan.
3. **Organizational Culture Assessment** - You need to assess your organization's culture to understand how your IoT Target Outcome will be received and supported. Mapping your IoT Target Outcome to your Organizational Culture highlights the areas that are not congruent that can turn into root causes of IoT project failure.
4. **IoTblueprint** - This removes IoT project risk by identifying all your IoT components, connectivity, vendors and expenses. The IoTblueprint Go/No Go phase gate reduces risk around missing components, lack of skills, underestimating complexity, and budgeting.

5. **IoTdeploy** – You examine the risks and issues of your IoT deployment strategy and process. You may have the skills and staff to Do-it-Yourself. However, using a pre-integrated and tested end-to-end IoT Platform as a Service solution will dramatically de-risk your time schedule and improve your financial return.
6. **IoTtransform** - The largest risks here are typically organizational expectations, accountabilities and introducing new processes. This is why the IoTaudit is so important: all the key IoT stakeholders are identified, how IoT data is to be combined with existing Enterprise data, and all tasks with accountabilities are assigned. With a shared IoT Target Outcome in mind, your organization can successfully realize your IoT Business Transformation.

IoTaudit: Reduce IoT Planning Risk

Having a well thought out and fully document IoT plan is essential to your IoT deployment success. An IoT network implementation is similar to other significant Enterprise infrastructure projects. But they are usually more complex in three ways:

1. Who specifies the hardware, network connectivity, security and software? IoT deployments often span Operational Technology and Information Technology domains.
2. Which organization will install, provisions, administer and maintain various components of your IoT deployment. There typically has not been a reason for these groups to work closely together as they will in a IoT deployment. New relationships and lines of communication will need to be created
3. Who is responsible for dealing with the various IoT data outputs- Alarms, Threshold Alerts, Real-time Monitoring, Data Storage and Data Analytics combining IoT Data with Legacy enterprise data.

This is why the IoTaudit was created to identify all these issues and interfaces ahead of time. Then you can negotiate all the issues ahead of time that will save significant time, money and organizational stress.

Using Premortem Analysis to Reduce IoT Project Risk

Projects fail at a spectacular rate. One reason is that too many people are reluctant to speak up about their reservations during the all-important planning phase. By making it safe for dissenters who are knowledgeable about the undertaking and worried about its weaknesses to speak up, you can improve a project's chances of success.

In a Harvard Business Review September 2007 article by Gary Klein entitled "Performing a Project Premortem" he described research conducted in 1989 by Deborah J. Mitchell, of the Wharton School; Jay Russo, of Cornell; and Nancy Pennington, of the University of Colorado. They found that prospective hindsight—imagining that an event has already occurred—increases the ability to correctly identify reasons for future outcomes by 30%. The article discussed how to use prospective hindsight to implement a method called a premortem, which helps project teams identify risks at the outset of a project.

This team was not alone in how important it is to use a Premortem analysis. Gary Ginther wrote: "CEOs attribute 21% of the reasons for success of a strategic initiative to "anticipating obstacles."

Premortem Exercise for StratGraph and Tasks Plan

Many people are aware of the Postmortem process when you analyze what wrong after your project died (failed). Instead, the Premortem technique has you analyze what might go wrong at the beginning of the IoT project - when the impact is nil.

The Premortem is a great risk assessment tool that has the following attributes:

- Empowers the people who would normally hold back their opinions and concerns.
- Places high creativity and originality – you are imagining the future
- Avoids Groupthink – the exercise is to think differently than everyone else.
- Dissenting opinions are encouraged and rewarded.
- Identifies future problems so you can see them coming. "I told you so" can now happen before the fact, not after the fact.
- Disaster and Delight scenarios can be created and discussed.
- The process is easy to conduct and document using the Premortem worksheets

IoT Project Premortem Overview

Projects often fail due to many circumstances. The Premortem Process is a way to understand potential barriers and complications to successful Internet of Things deployments BEFORE the project is undertaken. The idea is to identify the causes of failure, create actions to prevent or mitigate the failures. In an IoT Project Premortem held prior to the IoT project launch the IoT Project Team does the following steps:

1. IoT project Team thinks into the future and imagines and documents ways the IoT Project has failed.
2. Then the IoT Project Team brainstorms all the reasons that could lead to this failure.
3. The IoT Project Team then develops actions to mitigate these reasons for failure
4. The most important actions and review points are added to the StratGraph and IoT Task Plan.

Premortem Process and the IoTaudit

The Premortem Process is an important step in the IoTaudit. It should be performed first when the StratGraph is drafted and a second time after your IoT Implementation Tasks Plan is finalized. Performing the IoTaudit Baseline and Expectations phases insures the IoT Project Team considers many issues that go into creating a successful StratGraph and Tasks Plan. However, once the plans are created they must be stress tested by using the Premortem process.

Conducting a Premortem Workshop

The Premortem is held with the IoT Project Team and key Stakeholders (if available) in a live face to face meeting. Using email, teleconference or even video conferencing is not advised. The dynamics of having everyone in the same room drives a successful Premortem outcome. You will instruct everyone to be open and honest. Also, this is a brainstorming session so there are no wrong answers and politics/agendas need to be parked at the door. You must utilize a Premortem facilitator who is responsible for keeping the discussions open and the meeting on track. What you will need:

- Copies of the Premortem Input Sheet
- Flipchart paper (sticky top or use tape) for the scribes to take notes
- Small post-it note pads for voting stickers
- Larger post-it note pads for Reasons for Failure and Solutions

Premortem Meeting Process Steps

1. Hand out the Premortem Input Sheet and tell the Premortem team: "Imagine we have missed our Target Outcome Target completion date, and/or we have failed to reach our Target Value, and/or we have not realized our Target Return. Things have gone completely wrong in a number of areas. What could have caused these issues?" Spend the next 15 minutes writing down all the reasons you believed this failure occurred. What Baseline information was not collected or was incorrect? What Expectations where not collected or changed? What assumptions were incorrect? Where was the StratGraph flawed? What was incorrect in our Task plans: technology, resources, skills, funding, competition, market direction...?
2. After the 15 minutes, go around the room and ask each person to share one reason that has not already been mentioned by others. Write down all the answers on the Flip Charts for everyone to see. Go around the room until every failure reason is mentioned.
3. Now the failure reasons are prioritized by all the participants using 5 small post-it notes with a number 1 to 5 written on each. 5 means the highest priority, 1 means the lowest priority. Each team member places one of their stickers on 5 failure reasons. The post-its work well because sometimes people change their minds and move stickers. Add up the ratings for each failure.
4. After the top 5 failures have been identified, each team member privately takes 15-20 minutes to brainstorm interventions or solutions for the failure and writes these on their larger post-it note pads. They can write down as many individual solutions for each prioritized failure as they want.
5. Next, everyone places their solution post-it notes alongside the prioritized failures. Then the Premortem facilitator reads the solutions and clusters them into similar ideas.
6. Now the Premortem group reviews all the answers and discusses which specific intervention or solution should be prioritized and utilized.
7. The prioritized list of specific failure interventions/solutions and compiled into a list. The list is applied to update the StratGraph or Task Plan.

The overall Premortem Process looks like this:

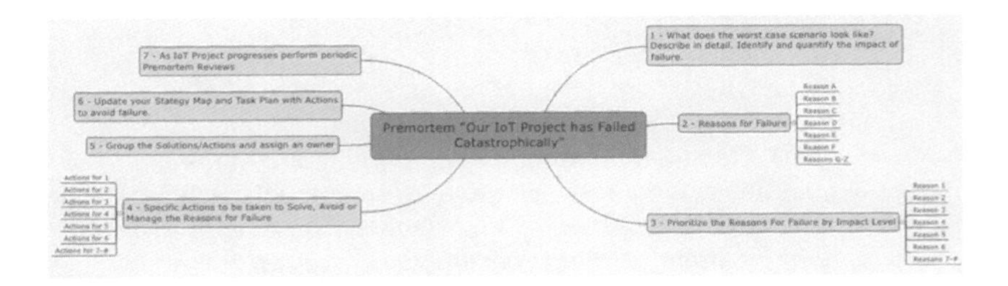

I realize the text is difficult to read, but all the IoT Premortem Process Worksheets can be downloaded at www.enviro-controls.com/iottransform.

IoTblueprint: Reduce IoT Com ponent and Cost Planning Risks

Creating a robust IoTblueprint is essential to significantly reducing the time and costs to deploy your IoT network. You can optimize the performance of your of your IoT network by identifying the integration issues up front. You will also reduce budget risk by identifying the most cost effective method of obtaining your IoT hardware, software and Connectivity

IoTdeploy: Reduce IoT Network Deployment Risks

Many companies are attempting and IoT deployment for the first time. The IoTaudit organizational IoT maturity assessment will document how well skilled and prepared your organization is to effectively deploy your IoT network. All companies who are looking to leverage IoT for their business transformation do not have everything required to build and deploy a robust IoT implementation.

Most companies are skilled in their primary business - Manufacturing, Insurance, Energy, Transportation, Healthcare, etc. So it's not surprising at all that these companies will need significant help with their IoT implementation. Companies who are technology focused may have some of the skill sets in hardware design, firmware, communications, software development and/or data analytics. But they will be missing key IoT skills and components that will come from partners. Companies building smart connected products will typically be able to handle the sensor integration and local area network connectivity (wireless or wired), But will typically lack the expertise with Gateways, Networks, Cloud Services and Business Software application integration.

The best way to reduce IoT deployment risks is to utilize an IoT end-to-end Platform as a Service IoT vendor. Often times IoT PaaS vendors have an industry vertical focus - Agriculture, Fleet Monitoring, Tank Monitoring, and Cold Chain monitoring, etc. An IoT PaaS vendor such as Enviro-Controls offers a customizable IoT platform that can address the needs of any industry due to the broad selection of Sensing modalities and flexible IoT Services software platform.

An IoT Platform as a Service will reduce risk in many areas through:

- A proven battle-tested IoT Architecture
- Pre-integrated IoT components
- Secure private mobile connectivity
- Customizable to meet unique requirements
- Secure easy to use IoT network administration
- Significant decrease in IoT Deployment Time
- Ease of remote maintenance
- No Capital Expenditures means reduced financial exposure
- Cost effective scaling as your IoT Network grows.
- Creates an IoT Corporate Platform standard for additional projects
- No Staff additions or extra skill sets required
- IoT Deployment can be managed by the appropriate internal organization.

IoTtransform: Reduce Business Transformation Risks

We have reminded ourselves throughout this book that "IoT is the Means to a Business Transformation End". In order to reduce risk in this IoT Project phase it is vital to take the following actions:

1. Involve key IoT stakeholders and organizations (both internal and external) in your IoTaudit planning process.
2. Involve all important IoT stakeholders in your IoT Project Premortem workshop.
3. Insure that all stakeholders support your IoT Target Outcome, will contribute the resources required of them in your plan, and attend your IoT project planning meetings.
4. Identify all the data sources to be used in your Business Transformation project and have accountability agreements

for data sourcing, data ownership, data storage, data analysis, and data reporting.

5. Create the project plans for your IoT Business Transformation. The member of this project team most likely will not be your IoT Deployment team due to the nature of the work to be performed. You may have business analysts, line managers, finance, supply chain management, marketing, sales and other personnel who will be using the new IoT data to optimize a business process or introduce a market differentiation offering.

Examine and Resolve a Major Source of IoT Project Risk

A key area of IoT business transformation risk, that is often overlooked, is how your IoT Target Outcome might be impeded by your organizational culture. Let's look first to understand your organization's culture and them map your IoT Target Outcome type to determine your best course of action.

IoT Success Requires Organizational Culture Change

Culture Always Trumps Strategy...

Over the last 25 years there's been three major organizational and business transformation change initiatives: TQM (Total Quality Management), Downsizing, and Re-engineering. Unfortunately, many organizations that implemented one of these initiatives did not reach their goals. Many studies have shown that 80% of companies fail to achieve their quality objectives. Companies that downsized saw their stock price fall behind their industry average a decade later. Almost 75% of firms in another study were found to be worse off in the long term after downsizing than they were before. In the case of re-engineering initiatives, the vast majority of companies surveyed reported little or no gain from their efforts.

A more recent business change process is Lean methodology. When a company is a start-up, Lean methodology may be quite effective as it is becomes the inherent culture of the small company. However, larger companies who have attempted Lean-based change initiatives seem to struggle without a definite change in the culture and behavior of the organization.

The main cause of failures with all these change programs is that the fundamental culture of the organization remained the same. Business transformation has an absolute dependence on cultural change. When change programs alter procedures and strategies - but organizational values, orientations, definitions and goals stay constant - organizations return quickly to the status quo.

IoT Culture Impact Assessment

IoT Business Transformation is all about driving new changes in your organization. Your results will depend entirely on how well your employees embrace the new processes and actions your IoT data will create. How well your employees embrace change is dictated by your corporate culture.

Culture fundamentally drives outcomes. It is why one team achieves results in spite of weak processes and tools, and is the same reason why another team fails to meet targets in spite of the best possible processes and tools. If you don't use Culture - it will use you.

What is Organizational Culture?

Culture can be described from the perspective of four elements:

- The implicit assumptions of the organization
- The conscious contracts and norms of the environment
- The artifacts of the organization.
- The employees explicit behaviors.

Your Culture is essentially "how we think and do things here". These actions are driven by:

1. Identity: "We are..." What is our social significance, self-image, mission and purpose
2. Beliefs: "We believe..." What are our values, norms, convictions and feelings
3. Competencies: "We can..." What are our skills, people, resources, plan
4. Behavior: "We do..." What are our services, processes, structures
5. Effect and environment: "We get these results..." What is our location, market, clients, results

Culture functions as the glue that holds organizations together:

- Reduces collective insecurity
- Provides a social hierarchy
- Structure for continuity
- Shared identity and familiarity
- Provides the vision for the future

Why does Culture matter?

Culture is important to your organization as it directs these 10 areas:

1. Organizational and Team performance
2. How organizational changes happens or does not happen
3. Recruiting and Hiring practices
4. Employee Engagement - Motivation, Absenteeism, Retention
5. Innovation
6. Production Efficiency
7. Customer Satisfaction and Loyalty
8. Brand, Image, Publicity
9. Market Share
10. Revenues and Profits

Can Culture Be Changed?

Yes, but you are never 100% in control. You can Influence it, evolve it, and develop it. There are certain conditions for successful cultural change:

- When procedures and strategies are changed, but the values, orientations, definitions, and goals stay constant, organizations will quickly return to the status quo. The same is true for individuals.
- Without an alteration of values and expectations, change remains superficial and short in duration.
- Unfortunately, failed attempts to change often produce cynicism, frustration, loss of trust and deterioration in morale. As research has shown, organizations may be worse off than if the change strategy had not been attempted.

Modifying organizational culture is a key driver to achieve IoT Business Transformation. A change in values, mental models, and targets should therefore be combined with a change in the context of how people work together. You must change the structure, procedures, and physical environment within the organization in support of your IoT initiatives.

It is imperative that your Leadership demonstrates both the will to drive change and the skill to implement change. But Leadership needs to understand their current culture and identify the specific cultural changes that are required for IoT business transformation. The OCAI tool can provides leaders with these insights and directions.

The Organizational Culture Assessment Instrument - OCAI

In order to assess your organizational culture, you will need a tool. This tool will be used with not only your IoT Coalition Project Team, but others in your organization who need to support your IOT Target Outcome. The tool must be easy to use and produce results that everyone can understand. One of the best cultural assessment tools in the market today is the OCAI.

The Organizational Culture Assessment Instrument (OCAI) developed by Kim Cameron and Robert Quinn from the University of Michigan is one of the most frequently used tools for assessing organizational culture in the world. Since its introduction in the mid 1990's the OCAI has been used by over 10,000 organizations. It is a vetted and well validated research method to examine organizational culture. The authors' most recent book on OCAI from which we will examine some OCAI material is: *Diagnosing and Changing Organizational Culture – Based on the Competing Values Framework* – Third Edition – Kim S. Cameron and Robert E. Quinn – Copyright 2011 by John Wiley and Sons, Inc.

This book is a "must read" if you are going to successfully change your organization in order to realize your IoT business transformation Target Outcome. It is widely available at bookstores and Amazon.

The OCAI survey tool is so useful because it makes people aware of culture and provides a shared reference on your particular culture. The results are quantified - which is useful for leaders and staff who prefer data represented as figures and facts. The OCAI involves and engages everyone who will be affected by your IoT business transformation. Using the OCAI, you will create both a Baseline Culture Profile and an IoT Target Outcome Culture Profile.

Cameron and Quinn invested a great deal of research into the development of the OCAI and based it on their model of the Competing Values Framework which they developed. This framework consists of four Competing Values that correspond with four types of organizational culture which we will review in a moment. Every organization has its own mix of these four types of organizational culture. This mix is discovered by completing the short OCAI questionnaire.

The Competing Values Framework

After extensive research Cameron and Quinn created a list of 39 indicators of effectiveness within an organization. After significant statistical analysis, two important dimensions emerged defined by:

- Internal Focus and Integration vs. External focus and Differentiation
- Flexibility and Discretion vs Stability and Control

You can see that these dimensions are essentially conflicting with each other. Internal versus external and a flexible versus stable. This tension between both areas is what drives the term **Competing Values Framework**.

Cameron and Quinn mapped four competing values on a graph creating four quadrants that correspond to four organizational cultures that differ strongly. The following diagram shows the 4 quadrant graph in order to map a particular organization's culture:

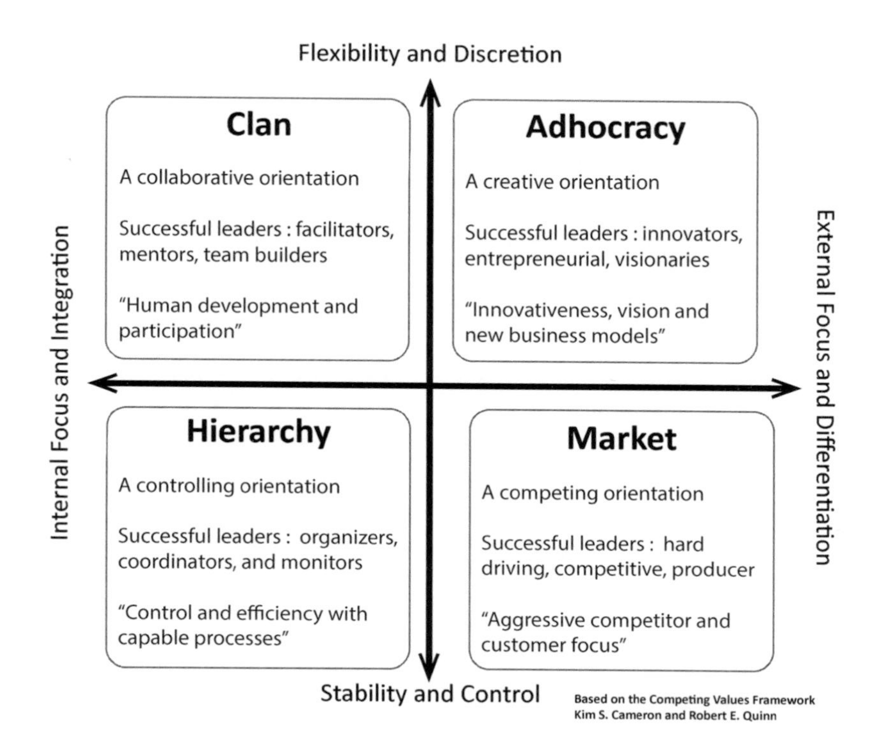

To the left in the graph, the organization is internally focused (what is important for us, how do we want to work) and to the right, the organization is externally focused (what is important for the outside world, for our clients, for our market).

At the top of the graph, the organization desires flexibility and employee discretion, while at the bottom, the organization wants the opposite values of stability and control.

The 4 OCAI Culture Types

Cameron and Quinn identified these four OCAI Culture Types:

1. **The Clan Culture** - A very pleasant place to work, where people share a lot of personal information, much like an extended family. The leaders or heads of the organization are seen as mentors and perhaps even parent figures. The organization is held together by loyalty or tradition. Commitment is high. The organization emphasizes the long-term benefit of human resources development and attaches great importance to cohesion and morale. Success is defined in terms of sensitivity to customers and concern for people. The organization places a premium on teamwork, participation, and consensus.
2. **The Adhocracy Culture** - A dynamic, entrepreneurial, and creative place to work. People stick out their necks and take risks. The leaders are considered innovators and risk takers. The glue that holds the organization together is commitment to experimentation and innovation. The emphasis is on being on the leading edge. The organization's long term emphasis is on growth and acquiring new resources. Success means gaining unique and new products or services. Being a product or service leader is important. The organization encourages individual initiative and freedom.
3. **The Market Culture** - This is a results-oriented organization whose major concern is getting the job done. People are competitive and goal-oriented. The leaders are hard drivers, producers, and competitors. They are tough and demanding. The glue that holds the organization together is an emphasis on winning. Reputation and success are common concerns. The long-term focus is on competitive actions and achievement of measurable goals and targets. Success is defined in terms of market share and penetration.

Competitive pricing and market leadership are important. The organizational style is hard-driving competitiveness.

4. **The Hierarchy Culture** - This is a very formalized and structured place to work. Procedures govern what people do. The leaders pride themselves on being good coordinators and organizers who are efficiency minded. Maintaining a smooth-running organization is most critical. Formal rules and policies hold the organization together. The long-term concern is stability and performance with efficient, smooth operations. Success is defined in terms of dependable delivery, smooth scheduling and low cost. The management of employees is concerned with secure employment and predictability.

Important Characteristics and Values that Determine Culture

When Cameron and Quinn were doing research that resulted in the OCAI, they were able to distill down the 6 key culture dimensions that are the major components that define an organizational culture:

1. Dominant Organizational Characteristics
2. Organizational Leadership
3. Management of Employees
4. Organization Glue
5. Strategic Emphasis
6. Criteria for Success

In order to obtain the data to build an organization's Competing Values Framework Culture chart, the OCAI tool survey questions were designed to assess the status of the 6 culture dimensions. For each of the 6 categories, survey respondents are asked to force rank each of 4 responses distributing a total of 100 points. Survey respondents are asked first about their Current Culture to create a baseline. Then they are asked the questions again about their desired future Preferred Target Outcome culture. Normally for each Culture Category there is a distribution of points across the 4 questions. But in the case of an incredibly dominant culture, a single answer could have 100 points and the other three questions 0 points.

The survey data from all survey participants is combined and then used to create an OCAI Culture Chart.

These are the 6 culture areas with their 4 response questions.

1 - Dominant Organizational Characteristics

- **A.** The organization is a very personal place. It is like an extended family. People seem to share a lot of personal information and features.
- **B.** The organization is a very dynamic entrepreneurial place. People are willing to stick out their necks and take risks.
- **C.** The organization is very results-oriented. A major concern is getting the job done. People are very competitive and achievement-oriented.
- **D.** The organization is a very controlled and structured place. Formal procedures generally govern what people do.

2 - Organizational Leadership

- **A.** The leadership in the organization is generally considered to exemplify mentoring, facilitating, or nurturing.
- **B.** The leadership in the organization is generally considered to exemplify entrepreneurship, innovation, or risk taking.
- **C.** The leadership in the organization is generally considered to exemplify a no-nonsense, aggressive, results-oriented focus.
- **D.** The leadership in the organization is generally considered to exemplify coordinating, organizing, or smooth-running efficiency.

3 - Management of Employees

- **A.** The management style in the organization is characterized by teamwork, consensus, and participation.
- **B.** The management style in the organization is characterized by individual risk taking, innovation, freedom, and uniqueness.
- **C.** The management style in the organization is characterized by hard-driving competitiveness, high demands, and achievement.
- **D.** The management style in the organization is characterized by security of employment, conformity, predictability, and stability in relationships.

4 - Organizational Glue

- **A.** The glue that holds the organization together is loyalty and mutual trust. Commitment to this organization runs high.
- **B.** The glue that holds the organization together is commitment to innovation and development. There is an emphasis on being on the cutting edge.
- **C.** The glue that holds the organization together is an emphasis on achievement and goal accomplishment.
- **D.** The glue that holds the organization together is formal rules and policies. Maintaining a smooth-running organization is important.

5 - Strategic Emphasis

- **A.** The organization emphasizes human development. High trust, openness, and participation persist.
- **B.** The organization emphasizes acquiring new resources and creating new challenges. Trying new things and prospecting for opportunities are valued.
- **C.** The organization emphasizes competitive actions and achievement. Hitting stretch targets and winning in the marketplace are dominant.
- **D.** The organization emphasizes permanence and stability. Efficiency, control and smooth operations are important.

6 - Criteria of Success

- **A.** The organization defines success on the basis of development of human resources, teamwork, employee commitment, and concern for people.
- **B.** The organization defines success on the basis of having the most unique or newest products. It is a product leader and innovator.
- **C.** The organization defines success on the basis of winning in the marketplace and out-pacing the competition. Competitive market leadership is key.
- **D.** The organization defines success on the basis of efficiency. Dependable delivery, smooth scheduling and low-cost production are critical.

Discovering Your Dominant Culture

The strength of your culture is determined by the number of points awarded to a particular cultural type. The higher the score, the more dominant the cultural type. Research has shown that strong cultures correspond with homogeneity of efforts, a clear sense of direction, an unambiguous environment, and high performance.

The extent to which a company needs a strong, homogeneous culture (instead of a varied, balanced mix of cultures) often depends on the environment. Is the environment complex and how flexible should the organization be in order to respond effectively to a changing situation? If a culture is dominant in one quadrant, change programs impacting other quadrants will require more effort.

The OCAI Graphical Results

The tabulated results are shown on the 4 quadrant Culture Diagram as a spider chart that often looks like a kite. Recall the 100 points are distributed across the 4 culture types, and the points for each category are plotted on the diagonals.

Our company Enviro-Controls took the OCAI survey. The resulting OCAI diagram screen shot (sorry it's a bit fuzzy) is shown on the next page. We are a small entrepreneurial company so it is not surprising that our Dominant Culture is strong Adhocracy.

Recall the survey questions are asked twice - the red culture map is our current situation. The blue culture map is our preferred future culture.

You can see the total points for each Culture type in the Now and Preferred columns.

As Enviro-Controls executes its Go To Market plan, our preferred Target Outcome culture is a move toward stronger Market-based.

How Do OCAI Results Relate to IoT Initiatives?

As we will discuss extensively in the next chapter, the reason you are planning to use Internet of Things technologies is to change some facet of your business. And we know that to realize successful business change your processes and people will have to change, and thus your Culture will need to change in some fashion.

Enviro-Controls OCAI Culture Map

Your profile :

	NOW	PREFERRED
CLAN	20.00	14.17
ADHOCRACY	43.33	37.50
MARKET	33.33	41.67
HIERARCHY	3.33	6.67

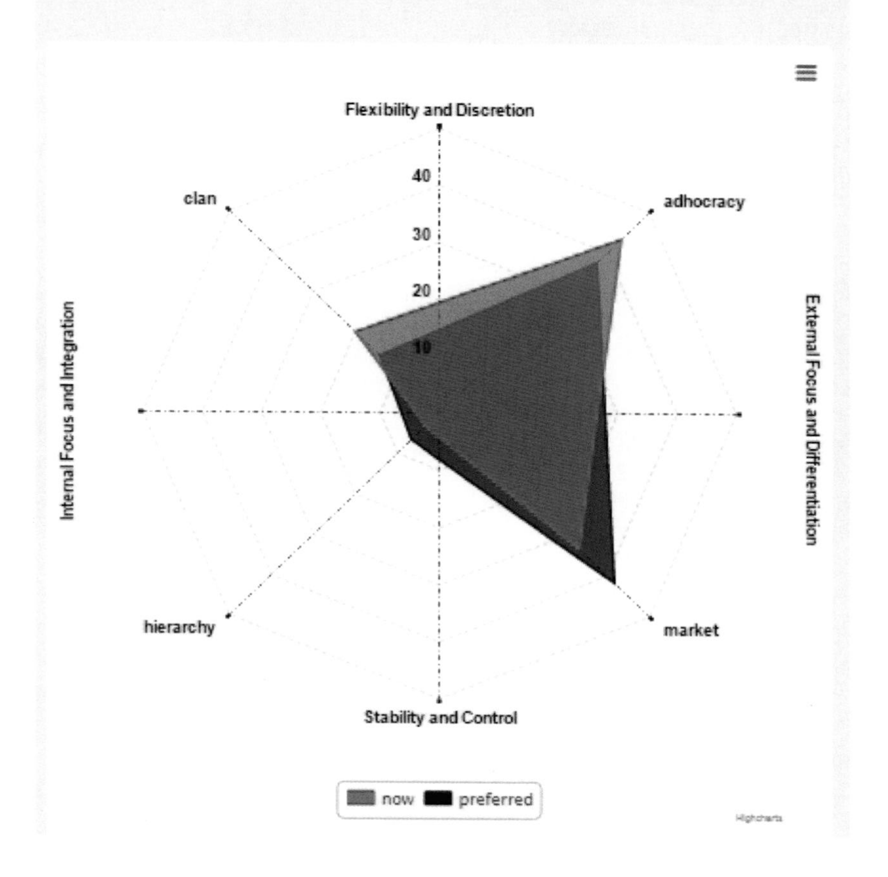

In the case of the Enviro-Controls OCAI chart we see a dominant Adhocracy Culture, a strong Market Culture and weak Clan and Hierarchy Cultures. So if we are going to introduce an IoT project that drives Entrepreneurial or Market-related change, it will be well received and supported.

However, if the IoT Target Outcome is focused on Collaboration or Control, there will be cultural roadblocks that need to be identified and neutralized.

Compare Company Culture to Industry Culture

Given that the OCAI tool has been used by over 10,000 companies, it is possible to compare your organization's culture compares to other companies in your Industry.

Enviro-Controls participates in the Information and Communication market area. When you look at this Industry segment where Enviro-Controls participates, you can see a marked difference in the Culture diagram of other more established companies.

Information and Communication OCAI screen shot diagram has a more even distribution of cultures across the 4 quadrants. The Dominate Culture appears to be Market with a score of 32.14. It is interesting to observe that these companies' employees preferred Culture is a move toward moves toward a stronger Clan Culture along with a stronger Adhocracy culture. This means the employees would like more flexibility and personal discretion, coupled with a move toward a more external focus and market differentiation.

Information and communication (1633 participants)

	NOW	PREFERRED
CLAN	23.62	31.59
ADHOCRACY	19.36	27.00
MARKET	32.14	22.61
HIERARCHY	24.84	18.74

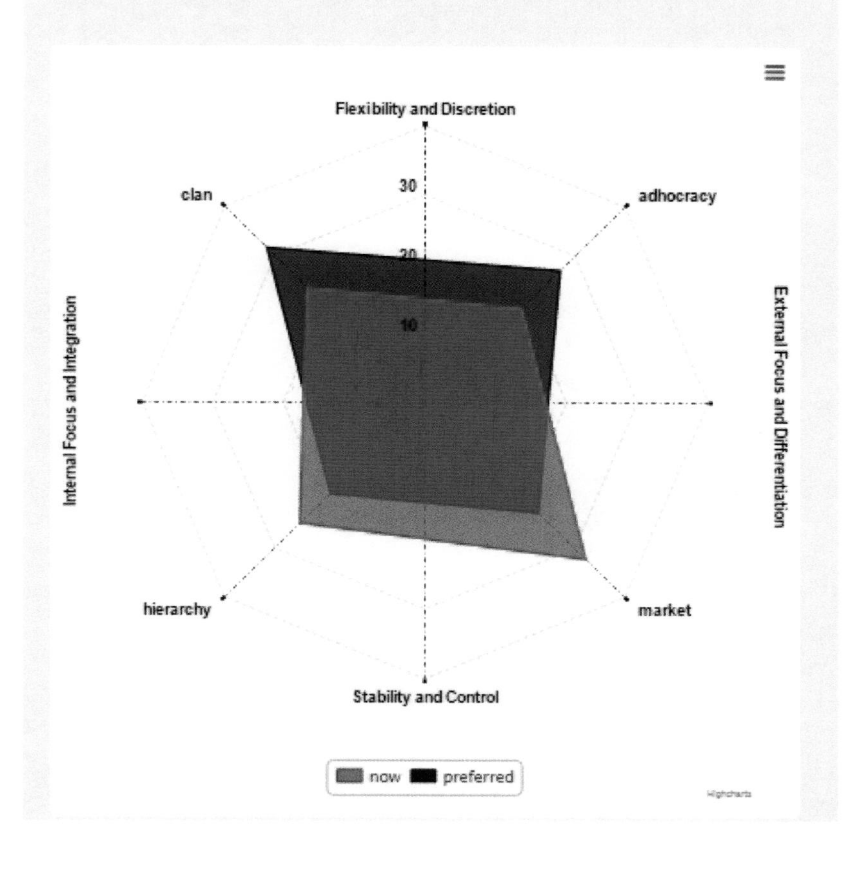

Compare Company Culture to All Company Cultures

When you look at the entire universe of United States OCAI data you can see that the amalgam of Now data has roughly a 3-way tie between Clan, Hierarchy and Market. Employees in these U.S. companies however, indicate in their Preferred data to shift toward more Flexibility and Discretion by moving the culture toward strong Clan with Adhocracy second. As Millennials become the leading component of the US job market, it is anticipated the trend toward Clan and Adhocracy will become more dramatic.

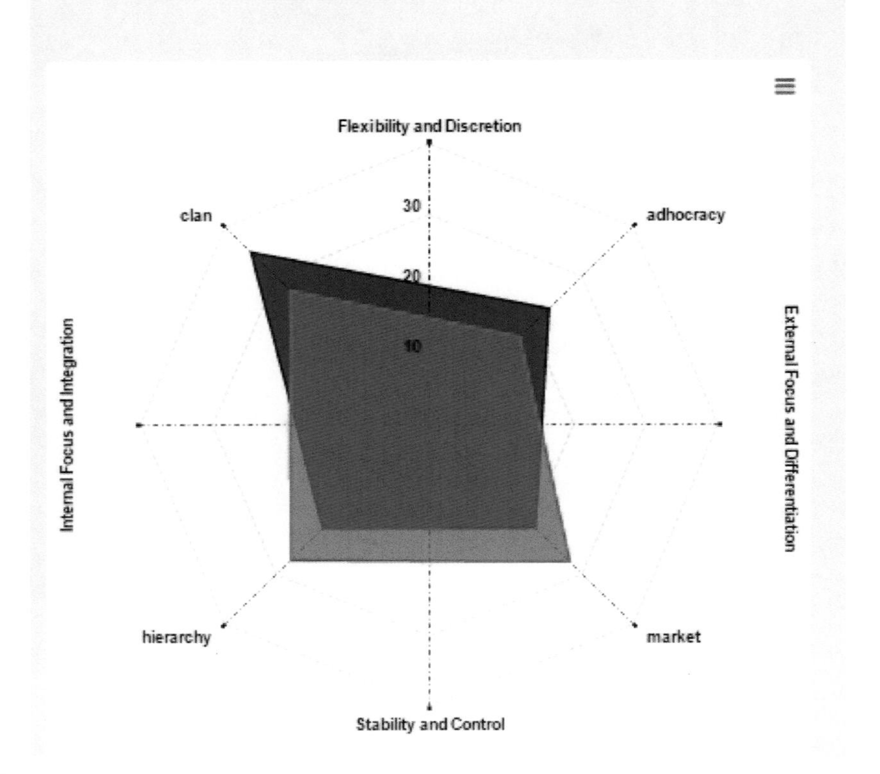

United States (25620 participants)

	NOW	PREFERRED
CLAN	27.42	34.90
ADHOCRACY	17.90	23.51
MARKET	27.55	20.76
HIERARCHY	27.11	20.81

Advantages of Using OCAI With Your Organization

In their book Cameron and Quinn point out six advantages to using the OCAI tool:

1. It is practical - OCAI captures key dimensions of culture that have been found to make a difference in organization success
2. It is efficient - the process of diagnosing and creating a strategy for change can be accomplished in a reasonable amount of time.
3. It is involving- the steps in the OCAI process can include every member of the organization, but especially involve all who have a responsibility in your IOT business transformation to establish direction, reinforce values, and guide fundamental change.
4. It is both quantitative and qualitative - the process relies on quantitative measurement, key cultural dimensions, and qualitative methods including stories, incidents, and symbols that represent the immeasurable ambiance of the organization.
5. It is manageable - the process of diagnosis for change can be undertaken and implemented by your IOT team within your organization which includes the management team.
6. It is valid - the framework on which the OCAI tool is built not only make sense to people as they consider their own organization, it is also supported by an extensive empirical literature and underlying dimensions that of a verified scholarly foundation.

Who should take the OCAI?

Since the OCAI is most helpful for determining ways to change your culture, the first step is to have everyone on your IOT Coalition business transformation team take the OCAI. But more importantly, everyone in your organization who needs to support or is affected by your IOT plan must also take the OCAI. Fortunately, the OCAI is a relatively inexpensive on-line tool that is easy to use. The OCAI tool is available on-line with user prompts and a results processing application. It is fast. Participants can fill out the survey in about 20 minutes. Go to www.enviro-controls.com/iottransform for the link to the OCAI tools.

Using OCAI Results with your Organization

As you saw in the Enviro-Controls examples, OCAI results are quantified and graphical profiles are recognized instantly. People take ownership of change when they define and customize their change process via their OCAI survey input. It's feasible to understand and identify the process steps for culture change with one assessment and OCAI workshop.

It is important to note that you should not use the OCAI if you're not intending to take action based on the outcome. OCAI participants will know their individual results and expect to see your organization's overall results. Moreover, if a gap is shown between today and the Target Outcome Culture people will expect something to be done toward change – and will be disappointed and disillusioned if nothing happens

Using OCAI Results with Your Organization's Mission and Vision

Apart from using OCAI results for your IoT Project, it is an interesting exercise to map your Organization's current Mission and Vision statements against the Competing Values Framework. The strengths and weaknesses of your mission and vision statements will become apparent when you map these elements. High-performing organizations have their mission and vision statement elements fall on quadrants of strength. If the elements of your mission and vision statement do not fall in areas of your cultural strengths, this incongruence is an indicator of a weak organization. What is happening is that your mission and vision statements are giving lip service to aspirations that your culture does not embody. So if you really believe your mission and vision is critical to your corporate success, then you need to change your culture to match these areas.

Changing your culture to match your strategic mission and vision statements can certainly be accomplished. Cameron and Quinn in their book give several examples of how companies changed their culture to support their strategic initiatives. For example, think of the cultural cycle Apple has gone through over the last 20 years. Under Steve Jobs they were originally a start-up adhocracy culture. Then as they grew they needed to morph into a hierarchy culture. Apple hired John Sculley to implement the stability and control required to produce hundreds of millions of devices. But then in order to revitalize the company, Jobs was brought back to move the culture back to an adhocracy resulting in the launch of many new "iProducts". Cultures can be changed, but only if the leaders of an organization are committed to the change and urgently communicate the reasons for the change constantly.

Let's now map your OCAI Culture results against your IoT Target Outcome to determine the best way to leverage your culture to realize a successful IoT Business Transformation.

Mapping IoT Change to Organizational Culture

Successful Change Requires Alignment...

You have conducted the IoTaudit System documenting your IoT Target Outcome, StratGraph, Tasks Plan, and your team has completed the Organizational Culture Assessment Instrument. The next step is to understand how your IoT Target Outcome and your Organization's Culture align - or don't align - which will be a problem to overcome.

Why is Mapping IoT Target Outcome to Your Culture Important?

If your IoT Target Outcome is congruent with your Organization's Culture the Business Transformation efforts will be aligned and synergistic. However, if your IoT Target Outcome is misaligned with your Culture, there will be organizational forces resisting and potentially fatally undermining your IoT business transformation efforts.

> **Key Take-away: IoT Business Transformations are most successful when the IoT Target Outcome is congruent with the Organizational Culture type.**

Identify Your IoT Target Outcome Type

Your IoT Target Outcome falls into one of 4 categories depending on the nature of your Target Area and expected Business Transformation:

1. **Control** – Optimize an Existing Business Process
2. **Create** – Launch New Product or Innovation to Generate New Revenue Streams

3. **Collaborate** – Improve employee Security, Safety and Connect Multiple Organizations
4. **Compete** - Deliver New Market Differentiation or Unique Customer Experience

These 4 types of IoT Target Outcomes are similar to the Organizational Cultural Assessment Instrument Competing Values Framework quadrants. Therefore, you can map your IoT Target Outcome to your OCAI analysis results. The following diagram maps the 4 IoT Target Outcome Types:

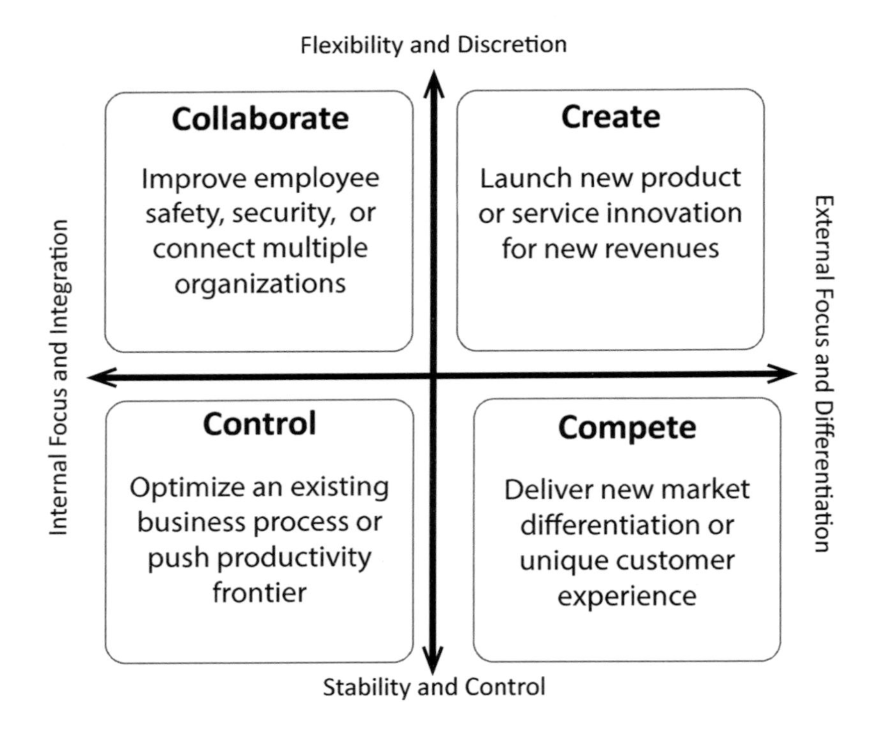

Let's examine what happens when you map your IoT Target Outcome to your Organizational Culture as documented in your OCAI report.

Mapping IOT Target Outcome to Your Organizational Culture

Your organization has completed the OCAI and you have your four quadrant culture map. Let's take a look at each of the four culture types as it pertains to IOT business transformation.

Clan Culture and IoT Change

This culture type is collaborative and the value drivers are commitment, communication and employee development. For change to be effective in the Clan culture, IoT Target Outcomes that focus on employee protection and inter-team collaboration produce the best results. Change leaders in a Clan culture need to have the skills of being a team builder, facilitator, and mentor.

IOT Target Outcomes that map well to a Clan culture are: Collaborate that improve employee Security, Safety and Connect Multiple Organizations. Collaborate IoT Target Outcomes are focused on improving the safety and security of people and facilities. Examples are: security video, sensors for fire, gases and water, worker tracking, and facilities monitoring of electricity, fluid flow, hydraulics, etc.

However, If your IOT Target Outcome is focused on one of the other three types, you must plan for a level of resistance. Especially, if you have a cross-quadrant IoT target outcome of Compete focused on delivering a market differentiation or new customer service. This may conflict with the normal day-to-day behavior of your clan culture. Your IoT coalition will need to address this with all the IoT stakeholders.

There is an interesting side note on Clan culture related to IoT Business Transformation. While Clan cultures are Internally focused, when their leaders are committed to business transformation and communicating effectively, they support their leaders whichever quadrant the IoT Target Outcome may land.

Adhocracy culture and IoT Change

This culture is creative and the value drivers are innovative outputs, transformation, and agility. This culture will more readily support IOT target outcomes that drive innovation, transformation, and agility to produce effective results. The change leaders in an Adhocracy culture need to be visionaries, innovators, and entrepreneurs.

IOT target outcomes that map well to Adhocracy culture are: Create - that launch new product or innovation to generate new revenue streams. If your IOT Target Outcome is focused on one of the other three types, you must plan for a level of resistance. Especially, if you have a cross-quadrant IoT target outcome of Control that is focused on optimizing the efficiency of an existing business process. This focus on efficiency and uniformity this conflicts with the normal day-to-day behavior of your IoT stakeholders.

Hierarchy culture and IoT Change

This culture is controlling and the value drivers are efficiency, timeliness, consistency, and uniformity. This culture will more readily support IoT Target Outcomes that focus on control, quality and improving processes to produce the best results. The change leaders in a Hierarchy culture need to be coordinators, monitors and organizers.

IOT target outcomes that map well to a Hierarchy culture are: Control - that optimize an existing business process and are focused on improving process stability, process control, efficiency, quality and on-time delivery. If your IOT Target Outcome is focused on one of the other three types, you must plan for a level of resistance. Especially, if you have a cross-quadrant IoT target outcome of Create that is focused a New Product or Innovation to Generate New Revenue. The focus on innovation and flexibility will conflict with the normal day-to-day behavior of your Hierarchy culture. Your IOT coalition will need to address this with all the IOT stakeholders

Market Culture and IoT Change

This culture is competing and the value drivers are market share, goal achievement, and profitability. This culture will more readily support IoT Target Outcomes that focus on creating a competitive advantage, finding new customers, driving profitability, or have a customer experience focus. The change leaders in a Market culture need to be drivers, competitors, and producers.

IOT target outcomes that map well to a Market culture are: Compete - Deliver New Market Differentiation or Customer Experience that drive new competitive advantage or focuses on customer success. If your IOT Target Outcome is focused on one of the other three types, you must plan for a level of resistance. Especially, if you have a cross-quadrant IoT target outcome of Collaboration that is focused on improving employee security, safety and connecting multiple organizations. This focus on innovation and flexibility will conflict with the normal day-to-day behavior of your Hierarchy culture. Your IOT coalition will need to address this with all the IOT stakeholders

IoT Change Leaders and Culture

After mapping your IoT Target Outcome to your Organizational culture, it is important to review the strengths of your Leadership team as "change agents". As we discussed in the previous section, when the leadership strengths of an individual align with the dominant organizational culture, these leaders tend to be more successful.

Key Take-away: Your IoT Coalition must have influential leaders at various executive levels who have strengths that map to your Organizational Culture.

Not surprisingly, the highest performing leaders in most organizations have capabilities and skills that allow them to succeed in each of the four quadrants.

IoT "Will & Skill"

As your IoT Leaders utilize the IoT Business Transformation System, there are two focus areas that must be highlighted and nurtured:

- **Will** - Everyone must Walk their Talk, Practice what they Preach and When the Going gets Tough – the Tough Get Going. IoT success is driven by over-communicating the urgency and benefits of the IoT Target Outcome. Along with staying with the vision when roadblocks arise.
- **Skill** - Since Leaders must be the agents of change they will have to change as well. Your IoT Target Outcome may be focused in one of your non-dominant quadrants. In this case, Leaders will have to acquire talents and traits that map to that quadrant to drive success.

Key Take-away: IoT business transformation fails when Leaders do not have a strong Will and they do not acquire new Skills and Behaviors.

IoT Project vs. Culture Mapping Output and Deliverables

As a result of mapping your IoT Project type to your Organizational Culture OCAI map you will have identified congruency or incongruency. In the congruency case, your IoT Project tasks will be related to watching for reactions from staff from departments who are not congruent with your dominant culture. An example might be finance who is inherently a controlling Hierarchical culture when your IoT Project is Creative.

More will have to be done if your IoT Project type is incongruent with your culture. Assign the roles and tasks for each of your IoT Coalition team members to work with people in each internal organization to solve roadblocks. This is very important work. As was discussed earlier, most change projects fail because the project team was unable to change organizational values, orientations, definitions and goals. If you do not attack these cultural incongruencies, your organization will never move from the status quo. All the hard work and expense associated with your IoT Project will be meaningless.

IoTaudit and OCAI Go/No Go Phase Gate

You now have done a significant amount of analysis concerning the viability of your IoT Project. Utilizing all the data from the IoTaudit and OCAI processes you can determine whether you and your team should move to the next step - IoTblueprint - to identify all the components, capabilities, and costs required to implement your IoT Network.

If your IoT Project is a Go - let's start the IoTblueprint Process.

IoTblueprint

Wow - So Many Moving Parts...

You have completed your IoTaudit, OCAI Culture Map, IoT StratGraph and IoT Tasks plan. Now it is time to put these into action. This chapter highlights the key steps for creating your IoTblueprint.

You will first need to research and select your IoT components at each of IoT Reference Model layers.

IoT is a hot technology space and there will be many products introduced from existing and new companies. These new technologies require new skills - which your organization may not have - in order to use them effectively. The Internet of Things will continue to evolve and will look very different in a few years. You will need to understand how to deal with this changing landscape.

Depending on your IoT requirements and scale of your IoT network implementation you will have options from full solution "End-to-End", to companies with point solutions, to Do-It-Yourself IoT. If your organization is starting with your first IoT application you should look for technology vendors and developers have established partnerships to reduce the cost and risk of integrating diverse technologies and systems.

There are several key technology drivers that have converged to make the Internet of things cost effective and scalable. These include:

- Reduction in component prices including microcontrollers wireless radios, memory and modules
- New standards for IoT protocols, data formats, software platforms, and data analytics

- Emergence of new and fast-growing vertical markets such as healthcare, connected homes, Thomas automobiles, and consumer products
- Major mobile operators are launching new IoT initiatives that provide cost-effective data plans. New low-power wide area networks such as Sigfox and LoRa are being introduced.
- New regulations and compliance activities are driving interest in adoption of IoT technology

The Status of IoT Standards

Emergence of IoT standards will eventually drive the shift from proprietary to platform-based solutions. The development of these standards will allow heterogeneous IoT devices to communicate and leverage common software applications which will be critical for the functionality adoption of IoT. However, IoT is a very complex space to create standards given all the forces in play: Governance, Privacy, Economics, Security, Legal, Partners and Workplace.

At the time of this writing, most of the integrated IoT solutions are proprietary so these companies can ramp faster. While we look towards the emergence of standards as a major catalyst of growth, many of the standards are still in committee and have not yet been ratified or rolled out. On the enterprise side, the setting of IoT standards will be a drawn-out process over the next decade, particularly with competing consortiums. Simpler standards-based solutions that are found in consumer IoT - such as Bluetooth Beacons communicating with mobile phones – are now rolling out.

There are several IoT consortium and resources for you to review:

Industrial Internet Consortium - www.iiconsortium.org/members - was started in 20 14 by 5 founding members AT&T, Cisco, GE, Intel, and IBM with 45 other members. The IC is focused on IoT use cases, reference architecture framework, and testbed prioritization. It is not a standard-setting body but it has established relationships and standards organizations to influence the standard making processes and enabler of IoT.

Allseen Alliance - www.allseenalliance.org - has 40 members and is working on the emerging all join operating system for IoT and open source framework started by Qualcomm. The ideas that into devices that support all join can communicate with each other without regard for which manufacturer made them which can extension technology they use.

Open Web Application Security Project (OWASP) - www.owasp.org - has significant content on IoT and web security.

The website www.postscapes.com has a useful IoT Awards page that identifies excellent vendors.

Starting your IoTblueprint Process

The key areas for your IoT blueprint fall into this 7 step process

1. Identifying your devices/sensors/controllers
2. Managing the communication and security of connected devices/sensors
3. Edge computing functions intra-site prior to data transmission to your central management system
4. Managing the LAN and WAN networks
5. IoT Services Software Platform functions
6. Securing and storing the data
7. Data analysis and visualization

The following diagram illustrates a complete end-to-end IoT deployment.

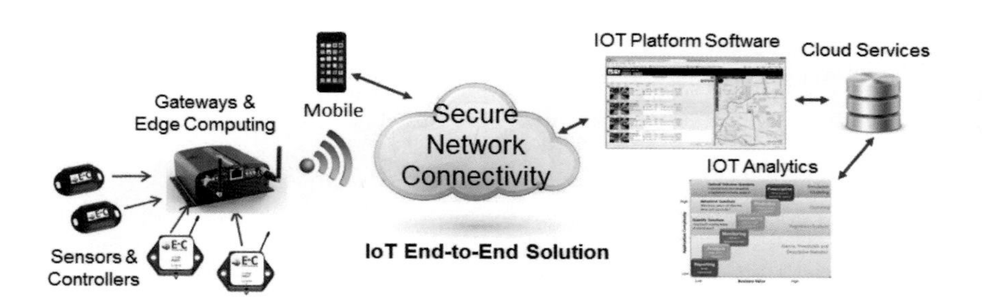

Let's look at each of the areas in this diagram in detail.

Sensors

Using your IoTaudit, you identified the sensing devices you will use to create your infrastructure data. The sensor devices may come from many different sources. Hundreds of companies specialize in unique sensors which may be wired or wireless. You may also have existing sensors that collect useful data that are isolated or utilize manual collection methods that need to be connected into your Internet of things network

One of the difficult problems in using sensors from multiple manufacturers the different protocols and data formats from the sensors. Some sensors might only be a contact closure or an analog or digital signal value. These readings will need to be converted into useful data format that can be transmitted to your central data collection point. Additionally many of these signals use a wired connection versus wireless connectivity. If you do not choose a single vendor for all your sensors, you will need to utilize the expertise of the system integrator.

Control Devices

Most Internet of Things network deployments focus on sensors. But often the desired goal is to have a sense and control network using controllers that are typically activators that perform a mechanical or electrical function. Examples are: closing a valve, lock a door, turn on a light, or set off an alarm.

Securing access to control devices is paramount. Sensor data interception by a hacker may not pose a significant business threat. But I hacker who can gain access to control devices can pose significant and disastrous consequences. So it is vital that cure protocols and networking be implemented from your sensor and control device all the way through to your IoT services software platform.

Gateways

IoT gateways are the devices that aggregate and connect the local sensors and controllers to other parts of the Local Area Network and/or the Wide Area Network. Gateways are available from many providers and have both wired and wireless interfaces on the LAN and WAN sides of the device. A great deal of focus has been placed on wireless gateways, especially in M2M style IoT networks where the assets might be moving as in the case of smart transportation.

Gateway Local Area Network Connections

Local Area Network connections can be accomplished via various wired or wireless media.

Direct Connections to Sensors and Controllers

An interesting challenge facing IoT gateways on the sensor/controller side is terminating existing Operations Technology (OT) physical interfaces such as:

- Contact closures – simple relays that represent a binary state
- Analog signals – a voltage, current or waveform representing various values
- Digital input/output data – can be simple coded values or a protocol of some form.
- 4-20 Current loop – used for many years in with industrial process control equipment such as pressure, temperature, flow and pH sensors, this analog signaling method uses 4mA as the lowest value and 20mA as the highest value.

There are also many legacy enterprise OT protocols that need to be terminated such as:

- Modbus – a serial communications protocol used in industrial applications for 35 years. It is a shared bus architecture connecting many devices to a supervisory computer.
- Fieldbus – another industrial standard IEC 61158 used for real-time distributed control. There are many competing Fieldbus standards including Profibus, EtherCAT and LonWorks.
- BACnet – is used in building automation and control systems is an ISO 16484-5 standard. It can run over various physical layers.
- CAN bus – used for over 30 years in vehicles and is one of the 5 protocols in the on-board diagnostics (ODB)-II vehicle diagnostics standard.

WLAN - Wireless Local Area Network Connections

The majority of new IoT sensors and controlling devices will access the network wirelessly. Wireless access is more pervasive, cheaper, and easier to deploy than wireline especially in retrofit situations. In many organizations Wi-Fi is available in the enterprise and may be a potential choice for connecting sensors and controllers to the gateway.

Sensor to Gateway Wireless Connection Options

Wi-Fi and Bluetooth are often used for wireless IoT connected home application. However in many commercial situations, sensors may utilize a different wireless interface that requires longer distance between the sensor and Gateway. More importantly, co-mingling your IoT network with your enterprise network may cause significant security problems. Here are examples of the may WLAN solutions currently available:

- Wi-Fi – is very ubiquitous in homes and offices and 802.11n operates in the 2.4GHz band and 802.11ac operates in the 5.0GHz band. Distance is normally up to 100 meters. New IoT version of Wi-Fi is called HaLow – 802.11ah – in the 900MHz band.
- 802.15.4 – is a popular IEEE standard for use mainly in the 2.4GHz ISM band also 866MHz and 928MHz bands. Range is 10 to 100 meters with a data rate of 250kb/s using carrier sense multiple access with carrier avoidance (CSMA/CA). Often used with 6LoWPAN addressing scheme that gives each node a standard IP address.
- Bluetooth - the newest version is Bluetooth Low Energy (BLE) using short packets at a maximum 1 Mb/s speed. The primary benefit is extremely low power consumption. The range is up to 100 meters line of site. There are several software profiles for various applications.
- Thread – is an IPV6 based 6LoWPAN wireless mesh network primarily for smart home automation applications. You have to be a paid member to receive the specifications controlled by the Thread Group comprised of several large companies.
- Weightless – is another LPWAN that use ISM bands 866/915MHz specified by the Weightless Special Interest Group. Intended for a campus or small metropolitan environment with thousands of end-devices connected to a wireless base station.
- Wireless HART – is used in industrial networking applications and is known as 802.15.4e. It can be used in a robust mesh network topology.
- ZigBee – was standardized in 2003 intended to be a simpler, less expensive, low power network with a range or 10-100 meters line of sight. Also based on IEEE 802.15.4, ZigBee range can be extended by using a mesh topology. Popular applications include home entertainment, smart lighting, personal area networks and building automation.
- Z-Wave – is oriented toward the residential control and automation markets. It is a proprietary protocol delivered on chips from Sigma Designs and Mitsumi that run in the ISM 866/908MHz bands.

- Proprietary Wireless Protocols – there are many vendors who use a proprietary wireless scheme usually implemented in the ISM unlicensed wireless spectrum bands.

Issues Connecting Gateways to your IT Network

We have examined many options for connectivity and communication protocols. You will need to determine your correct choices to meet your unique requirements across each layer of the protocol stack.

1. Physical Layer Protocol – wired, Ethernet, fiber, wireless for effective connectivity
2. Network Transport Layer Protocol – many different legacy protocols moving toward IPV6 for standards and scale.
3. Application Layer Protocol – puts contextual information around the data payload.

Important Note: you should examine closely whether the IoT Gateway should be integrated into your existing IT and/or OT enterprise network. If your Gateway has an external Wide Area Network connection, this may cause significant security and intrusion issues. If there is a way for hackers to get into the WAN connection of your Gateway, it will become a backdoor to your enterprise network. Disastrous consequences might ensue. Therefore, many IoT network designers are keeping gateways off the enterprise network and placing it on a separate IoT network that separates network and data conductivity.

Gateway Wide Area Network Connectivity

On the Wide Area Network (WAN) side of the Gateway there will be several interface choices as well.

- The Gateway WAN interface might terminate into your organizations local area network using Ethernet.
- The Gateway may connect to your organization's internal Wi-Fi network.
- The Gateway may be connected to external digital subscriber loop, T-1 lines, or fiber interface.
- The Gateway may be connected to a private wireless or microwave network.
- Or most likely, the Gateway will be connected to the WAN using a cellular network.

Mobile Wide Area Networks

There are several generations of mobile network technologies 2G, 3G, 4G and soon 5G. As the number increases so does the speed of data transmission through the network.

2G - was launched in the early 90's and was the first mobile technology to introduce narrow band digital networking. 2G is often known as GSM, GPRS or EDGE technologies. Many carriers are abandoning 2G networks to reuse the bandwidth for 4G and emerging 5G networks. So this is not a solution for new IoT networks

3G - was launched in the late 90's and introduced Internet connectivity to mobile devices. 3G as known as WCDMA or cdma2000 is currently the most common network for IoT/M2M connections. Most Gateways will use a small 3G SIM (Subscriber Identity Module) card to interface to the wireless network. Some carriers such as Verizon do not use SIM cards, but program the Gateway from the network.

4G LTE - was launched in 2012 and enables 3G functions with more capacity and higher data speeds. Newer 4G equipped devices tend to be more expensive and may be overkill for sensor networks with small data packets and long reporting intervals. For IoT/M2M 4G will become the preferred WWAN connectivity as device costs drop, battery life improves, and carrier costs decrease.

LTE Cat 0/1 - Since LTE is overkill for many IoT/M2M networks, LTE Cat 0/1 was introduced with reduced functions designed for IoT/M2M. Cat 0 data speed is 1Mb/s and Cat 1 is 10Mb/s and the distance is several kilometers.

NB-IoT - Narrow Band IoT is a recent variation using 4G LTE that uses smaller 180 kHz blocks. Data rates of 100 kb/s to 1 Mb/s are more useful for low data density sensor networks. NB-IoT can be deployed in an LTE network as a software overlay, or can fit into a re-purposed 2G GSM channel.

5G - is expected to roll-out in 2020 with a number of enhanced features that enable IoT/M2M.

LPWAN – Low-Power Wireless Wide Area Networks

- LoRA (Long Range Radio WAN) - is a LPWAN specification intended for wireless, low-cost, battery operated devices in regional, national or global networks. LoRa WAN is a product of the LoRa Alliance who plans to standardize LPWANs being deployed around the world to enable IoT, M2M, smart city and industrial applications. Designed to connect over long distances up to 16 kilometers, in harsh environments, and in isolated areas (e.g., underground). LoRa provides bi-directional communication between end-devices and enterprises via a gateway. Or many LoRA end-devices can wirelessly attach to LoRA Wide Area Network access much like a cellular network.

- SigFox –Is a wireless LPWAN technology as well as a network service. Named for the French company founded in 2009, SigFox deploys LPWAN using ISM band 866 and 902 MHz frequencies for low-energy objects. The network is limited to transmitting only small amounts of data with a wireless throughput of up to 100 bits per second and a payload size of 12 bytes per message. The company uses a cellular style system for connecting remote devices, and 'ultra-narrow' band (UNB) technology that enables signals to pass through solid objects, making it ideal for devices deployed under-ground or in rough terrain. In open space the connection range is over 40 kilometers. It also has an extremely reduced power usage rate, making the system practical for remote deployments that cannot be easily accessed for battery maintenance. The standby time for two AA batteries in SigFox connected devices is estimated at 10 years or more.

Design Requirements for IoT/M2M Connectivity

We have reviewed many different LAN, WAN, WLAN and WWAN technologies. The right choices for your IoT Deployment will take the following factors into account:

1. Data requirements – size of data packets, frequency of packets, transmit only or transmit/ receive (2-way), latency requirements. Examples range from a temperature reading every hour to streaming high definition video.
2. Distance from sensor to Gateway or Gateway to Cloud – ranges from a few feet to many miles.
3. Environment – wide temperature range, hazardous surroundings, electrical or RF interference.
4. Security – importance of protecting data. Is encryption or authentication necessary?
5. Power– AC or DC line powered, or battery powered. Source for energy harvesting? Identify the transactional and long

term power consumption of the device. On/off, sleep, power pulsing, etc.

6. Network topology – Point to Point, Star, Tree, and Mesh topologies. Identify the limits for number of connected devices including bandwidth constraints, unique addressing, etc.
7. Quality of Service - % uptime required, % down time tolerated. Service level agreements from wireline and wireless carriers
8. Wireless Spectrum – Use of unlicensed bands or licensed bands depends on bandwidth, security and performance requirements. Are there licensing requirements for the wireless technology or the network?
9. Cost – connectivity options will drive the cost of the device and connectivity. The more complex the connectivity, the higher the expense.

Also consider the nature of IoT traffic patterns are different than those of the traditional Internet. The differences stem from the fact that IoT devices will be in order of magnitude greater number than PCs, tablets, and smart phones, but the bandwidth usage per device can be orders of magnitude less. Think of a temperature sensor reporting a temperature reading hourly versus streaming HD video to a tablet. This means there may be a lot more signaling traffic on your network relative to data traffic, as well as a greater need for device management. Also, a greater percentage of the data generated may not be particularly useful. An example of this is a video surveillance camera where nothing new comes into the field of view for many hours.

Edge Computing

Edge computing is starting to emerge as a significant component of Internet of Things architectures. Several large companies such as Cisco, Intel and Dell are promoting IoT Edge Computing. IoT edge computing involves moving the sensor data analysis and control requests from a centralized site such as the IoT Services Software Platform down closer to the edge of the network. This is especially useful if you have a large number of sensors and/or a very high volume of sensor data that needs to be analyzed to generate a particular threshold or indicator. Not transmitting high volumes of data over expensive data conductivity to a central site can save significant money.

Furthermore, if the data analysis results in a control signal for a controller that is on the same side as the sensors, it is more secure to do the control on the same site and not be exposed to the external network. A net effect of edge computing is that decisions can be made with extremely low latency. For instance, raising an alarm for a process that has gone out of specification.

There are IoT deployments that will generate tens of thousands and even up to 1 million events per second. Edge computing configured as a distributed stream computing platform (DSCP) uses parallel architectures to process these high data rate streams. This approach is useful for real-time analytics and pattern identification. The data stays on site and WAN bandwidth charges are not impacted.

Secure and Private IoT Gateway Network Connections

The connection between your gateways and your central IoT software platform is one of the most vulnerable parts of your IoT network. You must implement one or more of the following security functions and capabilities in your IoT network:

- Data encryption ideally beginning at the sensor control device. At a minimum, encryption and security needs to start at the Gateway.
- Secure communications protocols between your Gateway and your IoT software platform
- A virtual private network between your Gateways and your IoT software platform

It is vital you engineer this part of your IoT network with security and privacy top of mind.

As we discussed way back in Chapter 1 security was a primary concern for many organizations deploying the Internet of things. Much of the information that is generated by sensors needs to remain confidential and proprietary especially in healthcare and medical applications. Another major concern is when you incorporate control devices to your Internet that of Things deployment. Control devices have the ability to change the state of your environment. Allowing someone to gain access to your control devices could be disastrous.

IoT security requirements will reshape and expand almost every enterprise IoT security program due to the changes required by software platforms and service scale, diversity, and function. Your IoT sensing and controlling endpoints may actually extend outside the perimeter of your organization and may actually reside at a third-party location. This adds additional complexity in communicating sensing and control information across the network securely. You will develop your initial IoT security based on specific, even tactical, business risk profiles. Then you will build upon the experiences of each subsequent IoT deployment to develop your common security IoT deployment scenarios, core architectural foundations, and organizational responsibilities.

IoT Services Software Platform

The IoT Services Software Platform is the central hub of your IoT deployment. This software platform enables many of the functions you require for your IoT business transformation including:

1. Sensor, controller, and Gateway device management
2. Network connectivity and sensor data formatting and normalization
3. Database for IoT data network management information alarm logs, user information, etc.
4. Event processing action management
5. Data analytics
6. Additional software tools such as mobile network management including SIM cards, GPS tracking, encryption, and security
7. Data visualization
8. External interfaces to other software systems using API such as restful API and JSON.

Your IoT Services Software Platform will dramatically reduce development time and risks while accelerating your time to market. On the other hand, there may be an increase in operational costs, new risks introduced by the platform, and single vendor issues. As you select your IoT Services Software Platform, there are several key issues to examine:

Cost – IoT software platforms are typically delivered as a cloud service with monthly base fee, a monthly charge per sensor and/or gateway, data usage and/or transaction usage fees. When you first start out, there are often nontrivial costs charged as an upfront implementation cost. Often there may be cellular network management and operational expenses.

Application lifespan and vendor stability – many of your IoT devices will have a long life and may operate for a decade or more. Many IoT service platform vendors are relatively small companies operating in a very dynamic market, and it is unlikely that many of these companies will remain stable for 10 years. The vendor landscape will evolve over time, as large vendors acquire some of the current IoT software platform products to jumpstart their presence in the IoT. For long-lived IoT deployments, it is wise to define a contingency plan for switching IoT software platform vendors. One approach to reducing the risk of vendor lock-in is to ensure that the smart devices use well-defined, open communication protocols that, in the worst case could be interfaced with an alternate IoT software platform.

Time-to-market – one of the key advantages of IoT software platforms is agility. Several platforms provide no code solutions for simple applications such as sensor monitoring and data visualization.

Value – IoT services software platforms can be flexible and agile. They radically reduce development costs, provide operational flexibility and also provide features in areas such as protocol management security.

Technical requirements – there are many technical details that impact your IoT architecture such as which communication security protocols are used, sensors, controllers and gateways connectivity standards, your required data throughput and latency, embedded hardware platforms to be used, etc.

Networking requirements – your current IT standards might use a wide variety of wired and wireless networks. So your networks might demand particular protocols and features that support a specific networking technology.

Scalability – cloud-based approaches for IoT software platforms make it much easier to scale systems, both technically and financially.

Security and Privacy - the information contained in your IoT deployment may be sensitive or even regulated. Given all the publicity around hackers on the Internet, platform security features are vitally important selection criteria.

Support - IoT software platforms that offer comprehensive support for developers may be less risky especially if your organization inexperienced in IoT. Open-source platforms are lightweight and open-source protocols may be costless, but will not provide the same level of support.

IoT Platform Partnerships and Services – IoT Platforms can be seem daunting to organizations with limited experience of embedded systems development, IoT software platforms and cloud architectures.

However, partnerships exist in key IoT areas to reduce risks and lower entry barriers. Several vendors now offer IoT is a complete end-to-end IoT platform as a service.

Once you have architected your IoT Services Software Platform you should examine your design in light of these four key areas:

Management - Your IoT deployment might connect thousands, hundreds of thousands or even millions devices around the world. Effectively managing this complex network will be critical to your IoT business transformation success.

Efficiency - Your IoT Platform will add efficiency for all your IoT stakeholders. New management functions and new customer experiences will be created. Examine and document how these efficiencies drive a successful IoT Target Outcome.

New Functionality – Your IoT Platform can drive new functionality and form new use cases from your IoT deployment by adding new intelligence to your devices, and providing additional communication interoperability between your devices.

Analytics – Your IoT Platform will manage, store and analyze the large amounts of data produced by your IoT Network. Over time you will add software for new analytics for different user groups – internal organizations, partners and customers.

IoT Data Flow Blueprinting

Your IoT Data will be generated and handled in a flow. Here are the major flow elements for you to document in your IoTBlueprint:

- Extracting Data - in your Baseline exercise you identified multiple sources of structured and unstructured data sources. You will provide context to the extracted data to produce alarms, thresholds, maintenance alerts, dispatch info, etc.
- Data Transformation - by compiling and linking IoT data you can create actionable information from the data interactions.
- Alarm Relationships - Identify which alarms can be combined to create new alarms and hence "Virtual Sensors".
- Use Cases - IOT data will be analyzed multiple ways depending on the Use Case you defined in the Baseline process.

- Failure Models - IOT data is used in advanced predictive analytics to determine preventive maintenance procedures.
- Operational Inefficiencies - Combine IoT data sources with scenario analyses to increase the visibility to infrastructure operation. This may uncover ways to resolve inefficiencies.

IoT Data Formatting and Database Schema

The currency of IoT will be the data, but only if this data can be translated into insights and information which can be transformed into concrete actions. One of the key tasks in your IoT blueprint is specifying your IoT data formats. Data is generated in different formats from your many sensor devices and this information need to be converted into a standard format so that they used in analysis and data visualization. You'll need to engineer your data schema in such a fashion that you can add new capabilities as your Internet of Things requirements evolve.

The emergence of big data technology for analytics has enabled enterprises to glean insights from significantly larger data sets created by IoT use cases in a more economical manner. The open sourced big data technology Hadoop for instance, can cost less than 1/10th of the cost of traditional database technology. The cost of storing and analyzing larger data-sets are falling and will improve the ROI on many IoT use cases substantially. It is expected that emerging Hadoop and No SQL database solutions alongside visualization technologies such as Spunk, Tableau, Qlik, and Initial State will be deployed in many IoT use cases.

IoT Database Design and Modeling

The basic steps for your IoT Database design team are:

- Produce a Conceptual Data Model – using an entity-relationship model or object oriented model. The data terminology for all your IoT data elements will be defined. You will have an external view model, a conceptual level model that combines the external views, and the internal level that identifies the physical organization of the data in your Database Management System (DBMS).
- Document IoT workflow – Identify what data is created where in each of your IoT workflows and the data retention characteristics.
- Create the Database Schema - this implements the relevant data structures and is often driven by the underlying database technology choice.

- Physical Database Design – make decisions that optimize performance, scalability, recovery, and data security including access control.

It is important to be aware that at the time of this writing the software industry is undergoing the most transformational shift and data architectures in the last 30 years. It shift is driven primarily by the need for new architectures to handle the scale and complexity of data generated by machines, web traffic, social networks, and the ever-increasing number of connected devices. While much of the data generated by IoT connected devices will at least be semi structured, it is believed the sheer volume, if not the complexity, will make innovative big data solutions necessary for many IoT analytics implementations. Internet pioneers have driven the development of two new types of data platforms to handle the big data phenomena – analytic and transactional. Hadoop is a software framework that supports large-scale computing and is largely used for analytic workloads. NoSQL (e.g. Cassandra) database solutions encompass a next-generation of databases that are often used for transactional use cases like IoT.

Security Architecture and Protocols

The proliferation of IoT devices, communications, and the massive expansion in data are creating a challenge for data management and security professionals. IoT implementations in many industries are going to pose specific security risks, as each industry faces unique challenges and regulatory requirements. This is especially true in medical and healthcare applications which may be required to abide by the HIPPA requirements. Additionally command and control IoT deployments that utilize sensors at power plants or telco equipment could present particularly attractive targets for cyber-attacks.

As related in the SANS Institutes's "Securing the Internet of Things Survey" in January 2014, roughly 75% of security professionals indicated the most vulnerable points and IoT deployment were the Internet connections itself, or the command and control channel for the device. There are vulnerabilities in device firmware management and device/sensor control we very important to enterprises implement more complex sensors and devices. Much of the necessary investment in securing these devices will take place within the enterprise infrastructure – next-generation firewalls, API protection, application control software, sand-boxing virtualization, and perhaps a new emerging security protocols and methodologies.

Data Analysis

Data Analysis is at the epicenter of your IoT network as this is where the Operational Intelligence (OI) is created. However, this is huge topic, and many books much larger than this one have been written just on the subject of "Big Data" analytics. (An excellent book on this topic is *Data Science for Business* by Provost and Fawcett.) So we will go through a summary of the IoT Data Analysis issues and opportunities that you need to consider as part of your IoTblueprint exercise. Let's start first with the BI Value chart from the Baseline chapter.

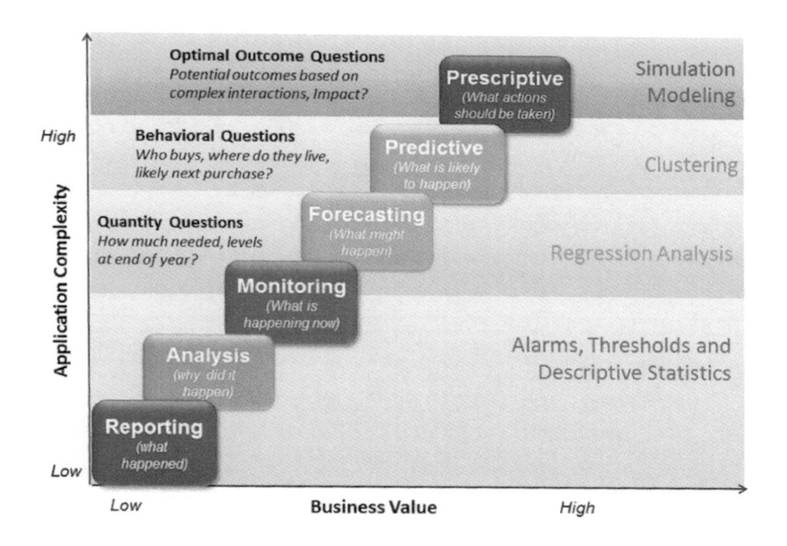

You and your IoT Coalition Team need to look at each of the 6 BI areas and determine the requirements for data creation, storage, analysis and corresponding actions to be taken for each:

1. **Reporting** - Document what IoT data will be collected and stored for use at a future point in time. This data might be: monitored parameters sent at prescribed intervals, threshold crossings, or inactivity indicators. This type of data is usually presented in a chronological data report, or filtered by some user selectable criteria. This is not real time data.
2. **Analysis** – Identify the analysis algorithms for each element of your stored IoT data. Document the cause and effect mechanisms across the IoT data set. It is vital to identify which of your organizations will utilize this data analysis and get their support at this point in the process.

3. **Monitoring** – At this level, real-time elements are utilized that dramatically impact the configuration and capabilities of your IoT deployment. Alarms, threshold crossings, alerts and other time-critical IoT data is received, analyzed and notifications are sent. You need to create and document the business rules that trigger your various alerts. Identify the people and systems that will receive alerts through various mechanisms. Given these real-time IoT data analysis capabilities will increase the cost and complexity of your IoT system it is important to optimize and minimize real-time alerting transactions to reduce operations costs.
4. **Forecasting** - Using your IoT data collected over time, document the data analytics you need to calculate. Identify the regression analysis and other data tools to be purchased or created. Identify which individuals will utilize the forecast data and how specifically this data will be used to achieve your IoT Target Outcome
5. **Predictive** – This data analysis is sophisticated and uses techniques such as cluster analysis. Most organizations for not have skills in this area. Identify the software vendors and data analytics scientists who can provide the tools you need.
6. **Prescri ptive** – Identify the sophisticated analysis tools that utilize your IoT data and trend analysis to prescribe actions be taken automatically or instructions to be passed to human operators. This often involves integration with existing enterprise IT or MOM systems.

Data Visualization

Much of the heavy lifting involved in IoT data is managing, storing, structuring, securing, and manipulating the data. But being able to analyze that data to find useful trends and insights requires powerful, purpose built applications. The use of embedded business intelligence (BI) or visualization products can be used as front and interfaces to add functionality to IoT web portals.

It is important for your IoT data users to see graphic representations of the IoT device data such as a map showing GPS locations of the fleet of freight trucks in near real-time, chartered trends in downtime for machine parts, or a graphed time series of biometric data from a health monitor. An excellent example is shown from the software vendor Initial State - check out their tools at www.initialstate.com.

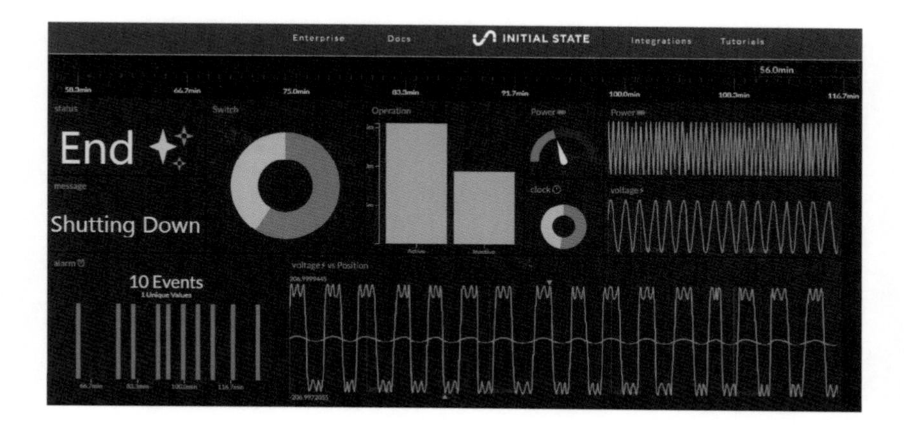

These data visualizations are used to drive important business decisions. Software tools such as Initial State require no IT involvement, and provide a highly intuitive software interface. This will allow your business unit managers to access the data driven by the power of your IoT deployment without having to increase your IT budget.

Connecting to Your Legacy Enterprise Software Applications

Often the IoT data you generate will be combined with other data from existing systems in your organization. Most common are:

- ERP –Enterprise Resource Planning Software. There are many different ERP systems of scale and complexity including SAP, Oracle, Infor, Sage, etc.
- CRM – Customer Relationship Management - Salesforce, Infusionsoft, SugarCRM, Microsoft Dynamics, etc.
- Finance – Accounting, Human Resources, etc.
- Monitoring and Management Systems - MOM Systems
- User interface devices - PCs, phones, tablets, etc.

User Access Privileges

Everyone involved in your IoT deployment will need access to various data areas and access user-specific functions. You will need to identify your user types defined by IoT data and function access. Once all your user types have been characterized, you need to insure your IoT Services Software Platform is programmed to support all user types.

One of the key concepts for your IoT Users is "a single pane of glass". This means that the human interface into your IoT data can be accessed on any number of devices including smartphones, tablets, laptops, PC monitors. The user interface across all these devices would stay the same for easy operation. In the case of smart phones and tablets, applications do not need to be downloaded on the device to access the data. Rather a consistent browser-based interface across all devices is used. This not only saves on training time, but also decreases the costs associated with maintenance of applications.

IoTblueprint Financial Checklist

To summarize this chapter, this is a short checklist for calculating the costs for the IoTblueprint phase of your IoT Business Transformation:

1. Engage with all your potential IoT Vendors to create you IoT Network configuration - Sensors, Gateways, Network, Cloud, Security and Application Software
2. Obtain quotes from all your equipment and software vendors
3. Configure your wireless and broadband network connections to calculate all your fees
4. Identify your IoT development partners - hardware, software, integration and secure bids for their work
5. Identify all internal resources to be applied to your project and determine how these costs will be accounted for in your project budget.
6. Create your IoT Network budget estimates
7. Add your IoT equipment and implementation costs into your IoT Project Business Case financials in order to review your Return on Investment calculation.

IoT Project Go/No Go Phase Gate Review

Using your Target Financial Return amount from your IoT Target Outcome statement and IoTaudit analysis, you will compare this IoT Return to your potential IoT Investment to calculate your IoT Return on Investment. If the ROI meets your organization's expectations, you move forward to the IoTdeploy phase. If your ROI is weak - work to find specific opportunities to increase your IoT Return and decrease your IoT Investment.

IoTdeploy

~~Some~~ (A Ton of) Assembly Required...

Now that you completed your IoTblueprint and have identified all of the components that you need to procure for your IOT deployment, it is time to determine the resources, talents, methodologies, funds, and project management needed to deploy your IoT network.

The key issue in this IoTdeploy phase is to determine how your organization will kit, configure, integrate, install, test, operate and maintain your IoT network. Depending on the your IoTaudit resources and skills assessment, your choices can range from all-inclusive Do-it-Yourself to completely outsourcing the work to partners. We will review the issues facing the various scenarios you might pursue.

Deployment Considerations

There are several key IoT deployment areas to consider:

- Plan for the number and intensity of initial IoT deployment activities required and then determine the amount of resources, money and time your organization can afford to spend getting your IOT deployment up and running.
- Once you've determined the right components for your IOT deployment, you need to ensure that your back-end systems can handle the additional data load creating from your IOT implementation.
- Don't underestimate the need for a device network connectivity management platform. You will need specific software tools to ensure that your IOT related connectivity charges are accurate and high network availability is maintained.

- Review your investment projections for software applications and data analytics required to generate the IoT Target Return you are seeking. The whole reason you're doing IoT is to create the data required to realize your IoT Target Outcome. Also review the leverage you can gain from leveraging your IoT data in other areas of your organization.
- Ensure that your organization understands the IoT fixed, variable, and recurring costs from all your vendors. A good example here is ensuring that your network data plan is appropriately sized for your data transactions. Data overage charges can be dramatically high.
- Make sure your organization has resources for smooth deployment. Most people in your company already have many things to do during the day and may not have sufficient personal bandwidth to support your IOT deployment properly. You may consider working with your vendors who can assist in the deployment and maintenance of your IOT solution If not, you will have to budget additional staffing to handle all the hands-on management and monitoring to run a successful IOT deployment.

IoT Deployment Decision Checklist

The following checklist is provided as a means to help you compose questions that will enable you to begin the discussions related to the IoT deployment value and ongoing management effectiveness of your IOT deployment.

1. Document the degree of time and resource constraints have you estimated with your IoT Strategy.
2. Consider the lifetime cost of your full IoT deployment.
3. Understand how your IT team staffed and assigned.
4. Consider the costs and benefits of outsourcing key parts or even the entire management of your IoT solution.
5. Consider the average life of IOT devices and applications was your plan for device outages.
6. Document how your company will recover and account for IoT system downtime and minimize conductivity charges.
7. Document the critical factors for your IOT deployment.
8. Consider the requirements of service-level agreements, device conductivity, network uptime, strategies for cost

control, scalability of data storage, and flexibility of the solution to grow with your company's vision into the future regarding analytics and applications.

9. Consider the end-user impact of conductivity or application problems.
10. Identify the degree of visibility your business units need into your IoT deployment for them to support your IoT deployment.
11. Document your expectations should you choose to address your IoT deployment with a managed services provider (MSP). Identify the specific capabilities you expect to add with managed hosted services that you do not currently have internally. List your make or break factors.
12. Negotiate and document how your organizations are committed and ready in terms of personnel dollars, agreed-upon strategy and culture change to deploy your IOT solution by your IoT Target Date.
13. Identify who will do Initial customization and professional services.
14. Understand IoT device certifications - required in one country - or in multiple countries?
15. Document which data and/or analytics applications require enhancements. Identify who will perform the work.
16. Identify who will perform ongoing customization - will outside professional services be used.

Variable Cost Items

There are variable cost IoT deployment items that you should assess with your perspective solution vendors to minimize your total cost of ownership:

- Data usage costs from wireless and broadband WAN providers.
- Examine using seamless network switching between the higher cost and lower-cost networks and higher speed and lower speed networks.
- Co-mingle devices with high and low usage on the same data plan. Attempt to aggregate your data on one plan for savings
- Look to avoid cellular data plan overage costs because of malfunctioning devices and applications.

- Watch out for mid-cycle rate plan changes.
- Lifecycle costs in the event of device suspend/resume actions.
- Device upgrade or repair costs.

It will help to stage device activations. Consider the costs of large quantities versus small quantities over the course of the IoT roll-out.

Skills and Accountabilities to be Assigned

If you're going to deploy your IoT network yourself, you will need to assemble a team of following skills:

- Procurement staff to establish an IoT supply chain for your equipment, software and maintenance.
- On-site staff for Sensor and Gateway installation
- Network engineering staff
- Software platform installation and cloud services set-up
- Software engineering for IOT software platform
- Software analysts for integrating IOT data into current enterprise system such as ERP, CRM and accounting.
- Staff for ongoing provisioning, monitoring and maintenance of your IOT network

Utilizing an IoT Platform as a Service Solution

A major recent trend in Internet of Things deployments is an IoT Platform as a Service offering. An IoT PaaS solution contains all the components needed for a complete end-to-end solution. Over the last few years several vertical-specific solutions have been available from large companies that solved a specific IoT use case. Examples are Honeywell Fire Protection systems, Emerson Industrial Controls, and Trane HVAC control systems.

Recent advances in IoT technologies have enabled flexible IoT PaaS offerings that can be easily customized for specific end-user customer needs. An excellent example of an IoT PaaS is the Enviro-Controls IoT Smart Overlay™ Platform as a Service. The Enviro-Controls solution utilizes 28 different types of sensors to meet the requirements of almost any sensing application. These sensors wirelessly connect to a Cellular Gateway that aggregates all the sensor information onto a single wireless or wired broadband connection. The Gateway connects over a secure wireless Virtual Private Network (VPN) to an IoT Services Software Platform that provides all the data filtering, storage, alarming, thresholds, reports, user screens and data analytics interfaces. A diagram of the Enviro-Controls IoT Smart Overlay is shown on the next page.

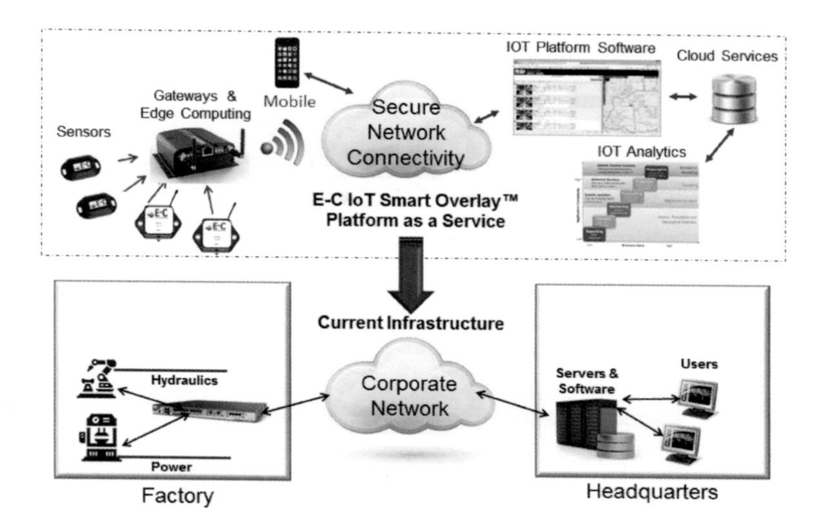

At the top of this diagram is the IoT Smart Overlay PaaS Solution. Underneath is an example of an existing end-user infrastructure consisting of a factory with machines, hydraulics, and power to be monitored by IoT sensors. This factory network is connected to the company's headquarters site that houses the IT servers and software. The next diagram shows the IoT Smart Overlay integrated into the existing infrastructure. There are only 2 points of contact - the sensors and the IoT data interface to the existing IT servers and data.

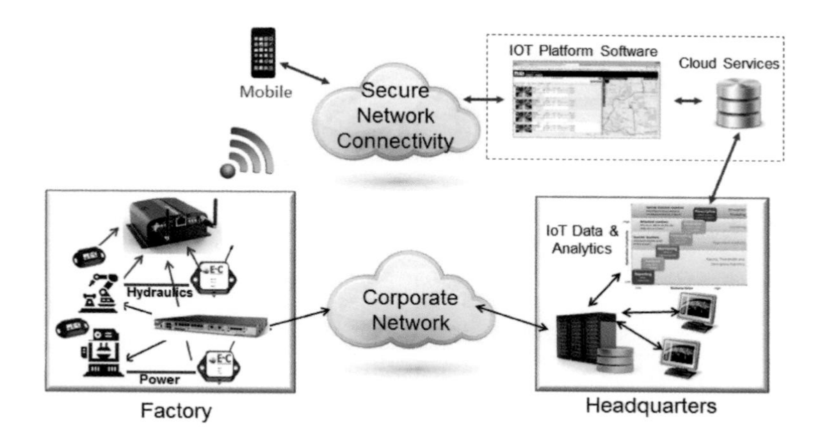

There are several important advantages to an IoT PaaS:

1. Sensors can be flexibly selected, configured and deployed on existing infrastructure.
2. The Sensor connections utilize their own wireless network and is not attached to the company's existing LAN.
3. The Gateway connects to a separate secure wireless network that is not attached to the company's LAN or WAN.
4. Most importantly, the Gateway to IoT Services Software Platform secure network is not connected to the Public Internet in any fashion. This prevents access to hackers and malicious threats.
5. The IoT Services Platform is pre-configured to automatically connect to the Sensors and Gateway when powered on.
6. The IoT Services Software Platform utilizes standard application programming interfaces (APIs) to existing IT systems and IoT data analytics databases and applications.

Details on the Enviro-Controls IoT Smart Overlay PaaS are available here: http://enviro-controls.com/iot-smart-overlay

IoTdeploy Summary

Your choice of IoT network deployment will depend on your organization's capabilities, resources, budget, schedule and risk tolerance. You may choose to completely do-it-yourself, completely outsource to partners, or utilize a mix of in-house/outsource. Once your Internet of Things network is implemented, you will move into the IoTtransform phase where the real value of achieving your IOT Target Outcome is realized.

IoTtransform

IoT is the Means to this End...

Everything we have done up to this point has been leading to the fourth phase of the IoT Business Transformation System - IoTtransform. Now you will use the new IoT data from your IoT deployment to drive the changes required to achieve your IoT Target Outcome. You have used the first 6 IoT Business Transformation System processes:

The 8 Foundations for Successful IoT Business Transformation

1. IoT Target Outcome - your IoT success vision urgently driven by the Leadership Team
2. Baseline and Backtrack from Current Value to Target Value
3. Expectations of all IoT Stakeholders understood by IoT Coalition Team
4. StratGraph visualizing how you will realize IoT success.
5. Tasks Plan with single point of accountabilities continuously communicated by your IoT Coalition
6. Blueprint and Deploy IoT solution implemented using milestones with short term wins that are celebrated
7. Change and Communicate - drive culture change, deploy new processes, celebrate wins, reward accountable team members
8. Anchor new Business Transformation processes become standard habit to drive IoT Target Outcome success

Now we will pursue processes 7 and 8 which will complete the journey to a successful IoT Target Outcome.

IoT Target Outcome Achievement

After you identified the gap in your Target Outcome statement, you did a root cause analysis and documented the barriers that had to be overcome to achieve your Target Value. You created your IoTblueprint and deployed your IoT solution. Your goal has been to cost effectively provide the sensing data and control mechanisms needed to resolve the Current Value-Target Value gap issues. Now comes the pivotal phase - creating the changes in processes and people to drive IoT Business Transformation success.

People and Process Drive Business Transformation

In order to create change in your organization, there must be personal points of accountability for each of the affected business processes. These change owners may be part of the IoT Coalition Team, but most likely they are new to the process given their day-to-day responsibilities. Process change falls into two categories:

- **Enhanced Process** - an existing process is changed by utilizing the new IoT data often in combination with existing process data. In your Baseline process, you identified the person or department responsible for the current process who will need to be convinced these IoT-related changes are a "good thing". Your Expectations process should have driven negotiations the accountable owners.
- **New Business Processes** - this process did not exist before and is something new to the organization. These types of business transformations are often difficult to accomplish due to "we don't do it this way" or "fear of the unknown". Your Baseline process identified that since the process is new, there are no current owners. At this point, you have to identify the person who will accept the accountability for owning the new process.

IoT Transformation and Organizational Culture

Recall earlier that we used the OCAI tool to survey your organization and determine your culture. A dominant culture style emerged. We then identified your IoT Target Outcome type and mapped that to your culture grid. As part of the IoTtransform process, we now need to understand the impact of the mapping:

- **Congruency of Culture and IoT Target Outcome** - this is good news. Your organization should inherently embrace your IoT Target Outcome as it does not feel threatening at a high level. There will still be the normal push-back to change, but your organization should react positively to the "why we are doing this."

- **Incongruency of Culture and IoT Target Outcome** - this often is bad news depending on the extent of the mismatch. Your organizational Competing Values Framework "kite" diagram shows the relative strength of each culture type. If your IoT Target Outcome falls in the quadrant of your weakest culture component, you will have to create plans to overcome your organization's culture bias to reject the IoT-related changes.

Commitment from the Top with Urgency

The number one way change happens in an organization is that senior leadership effectively communicates their support of your IoT Project. These communications must be clear, identify the urgency for achieving the success, and are inspirational to everyone involved in the IoT change. Furthermore, senior leaders must insure their downline managers support the IoT business transformation. The entire management team needs to be on board, and that is why the Expectations process is so important. Employees will embody the attitudes of their managers. So if the managers are not on board, the IoT change process will falter.

Crash through barriers using Continuous Communication

It is almost impossible for senior leaders to under-communicate during this phase of the IoT change process. It is vital that the senior leaders communicate their support to all the IoT stakeholders and affected parties. They must show great interest in the process changes, support accountable personnel with their change deliverables, and celebrate short-term wins.

IoT Coalition Team Focus Changes

At this stage of your IoT Business Transformation project, focus is placed on changing the business processes that drive the achievement of your Target Value. Often this means the IoT Coalition members responsible for the Strategic Focus Areas of Process, Staff and Skills, and Finance will need to take a more visible leadership role.

Process Change Owners Consensus Through Shared Expectations

Now that IoT business transformation activities are taking place, many new people will become aware of the change program. Focus on the employees and IoT stakeholders who will help lead the IoT charge. Don't try to get everyone on board. Let the passive majority wait to see IoT success and they will jump on board as the risk of failure is lower.

Continue Using your IoT StratGraph and TASKs plan

You used your both of these tools to define and deploy your IoT network. But remember the final phase in both these tools is Business Transformation. This phase has tasks of it's own in each of the Strategic Focus Areas. At this time you need to find and celebrate small wins by highlighting team member accomplishments.

Key IoT-related Process Change Actions

Your IoT StratGraph will have Strategy Action Areas related to process change that your IoT Implementation TASKs Plan will document showing what has to be done, by whom, and when. Tangible examples include:

- New Personnel Assignments
- New Process Charts
- Process Change Orders
- New Training Manuals
- New Reports and Dashboards
- New Product/Service Launch Plans and Collaterals

Anchoring your IoT Business Transformation

The 8th and final step of the IoT Business Transformation System is to anchor your new IoT-related changes so that they become organizational habits. Creating new habits means teaching personnel to act differently. One of the most effective ways to establish new habits is to use the "4 C's" method.

Copy,Coach,Correct and Celebrate to Change Habits

These 4C's determine how IoT business transformation is anchored in interactions at the behavioral level. We discussed earlier how important it is that all managers in an organization supports the IoT-related changes. This process is the physical manifestation of that support.

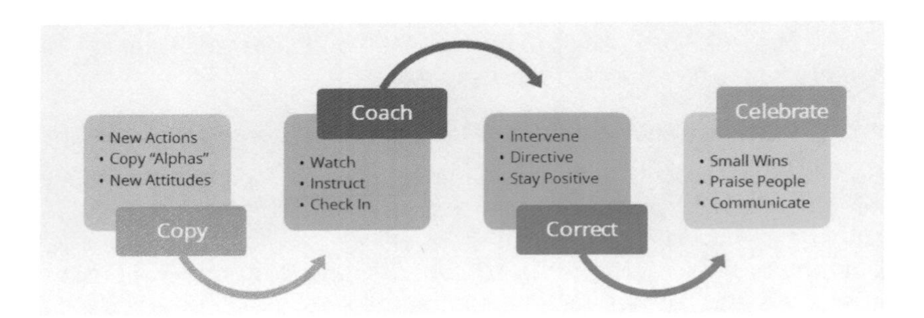

1. **Copy** - employees who are new to the new IoT-related change processes copy "alpha" employees actions and attitudes.
2. **Coach** – Managers and peers instruct the accountable personnel when asked, or more likely "when they think they should".
3. **Correct** – Managers and peers will intervene with "positive directive coaching" when they see inappropriate actions being taken by accountable personnel after previous coaching.
4. **Celebrate** - Managers and peers will identify when key milestones are successfully achieved and celebrate these accomplishments publicly with the accountable personnel.

It is important to remember that accountability is used in the positive sense. So Coaching and Correcting is always done in a positive manner and in a spirit of support.

Also note that each phase of the 4C's Change Process depends on effective communication. Not only do your Leaders need to communicate their support of your IoT project as we discussed earlier, but everyone on your IoT Coalition must work to over-communicate successes.

Executing the Final Step of your Strategy Realization Process

The last step of your StratGraph is Business Transformation. Your IoT Tasks Plan will have a series of tasks that are constructed to drive the changes in your organization to achieve your IoT Target Outcome. The most important thing to remember is that the team members assigned to execute these changes were most likely not those accountable for planning, blueprinting and deploying your IoT Network. So special attention needs to be paid to those accountable for the day to day change mechanisms.

Building Upon the Foundation of Your IoT Success

Successfully anchoring the changes that achieved your IoT Target Outcome will provide your organization with a significant competitive advantage. You now have an excellent IoT platform and processes to serve as the base for your future IoT initiatives . You will build upon your intelligent devices, smart gateways, secure networks, IoT Services Software, Data Analytics, Data Visualization, newly optimized business processes, and new revenue streams.

Your organization has the opportunity to leverage your IoT platform across many areas and eliminate the use of disparate networks, devices, hardware and software that come from "one-off" projects. You can optimize your support staff to by utilizing IoT embedded intelligence and smart systems. Most importantly you will reduce time to market, overall costs, and risks by building upon your IoT Platform.

Take Action Now and Realize the Benefits

Using the Internet of Things to transform you business can be a daunting task. Given the complexity of both IoT technology and the organizational change process, you may be wary of taking on an IoT Project. But the rewards of IoT are real and organizations around the world are profiting from using the Internet of Things. Using the structured processes and tools in this book provide a solid foundation for your IoT planning, deployment and business transformation.

Additional resources are available are available at www.enviro-controls.com/iottransform. You can also contact us on this page if you would like to discuss your IoT requirements and potential solutions.

Final Thoughts and Taking Action

Action is the Foundational Key to All Success...

Congratulations on your arrival here. We covered a lot of ground in discussing the systems, tools, strategies, processes and tasks you will need to implement to realize your IoT Business Transformation success. Make no mistake, an Internet of Things deployment and the subsequent business transformation effort is an extraordinarily difficult undertaking. However, the financial rewards for business process optimization and/or market differentiation can be significant. The IoT Business Transformation System provides the essentials for Internet of Things success. Let's review the process you should follow to realize your IoT business transformation:

- **IoT Target Outcome and Vision** - create your "We will improve Target Area from Current Value to Target Value by Target Date achieving Target Financial Return" and then paint the vision.
- **Baseline and Backtrack** - Perform root cause analysis on the Current Value to Target Value gap. Research and document all the IoT-related facets of your current state. Backtrack from future your IoT Target Value to your current state. Link your findings.
- **Expectations** - Interview all IoT stakeholders to document their expectations. Negotiate and document roles and accountabilities
- **StratGraph** - Using IoT Target Outcome Vision, Baseline and Expectations identify Strategic Focus Areas, Strategic Phases, Strategic Action Areas to realize IoT Business Transformation.

- **TASKs Plan** - Using StratGraph to create a detailed IoT implementation plan using Time, Accountability, Steps and Keep Score. Use Project tracking and collaboration tools.
- **IoT Culture Impact** - use OCAI tool to determine Dominant Culture and map to IoT Target Outcome type to determine congruency/incongruency.
- **IoTblueprint** - identify all hardware, software, network and data analysis required for robust IoT implementation.
- **IoTdeploy** - determine the best methods for deploying your IoT network, internal resources and/or external partners including IoT Platform as a Service, and Managed Service Partners.
- **Change and Communicate** - Institute new and enhanced IoT-related processes and procedures. Senior leadership must communicate IoT importance and urgency.
- **Anchor Transformation** - IoT related changes become habit. Use Copy, Coach, Correct and Celebrate methods to engage and energize your organization.

By using the information in this book, you will be miles ahead of almost all other organizations attempting to utilize the Internet of Things in their business. You will be using a structured planning approach that identifies financial outcomes, understands the impact of culture, and intelligently reduces the risks inherent in a complex IoT project.

It is often prudent to utilize outside expertise in IoT projects. The team at Enviro-Controls is helping organizations all around the world succeed with their IoT initiatives. We can be contacted at www.enviro-controls.com/iottransform for a no-obligation consultation.

It's a competitive world and the time to start your IoT journey is now. Thank you for using this book as one of your resources. I wish you great success with your Internet of Things business transformation.

I would appreciate any feedback you may have on this book - changes, enhancements, missing topics, etc. Please send them to steve.grady@enviro-controls.com.

Now it is time to turn your IoT Target Outcome into IoT business transformation success.

Go Get 'em!

References and Resources

So Much to Read, So Little Time...

Given the complex nature of Internet of Things projects ,there are many useful resources you can use to inform and direct your IoT Project. Here are several books and articles that were either referenced in this book or are recommended as excellent resources.

References

These books and articles are referenced in this book.

Roger Connors and Tom Smith, *Change the Culture, Change the Game*, Portfolio/Penguin, 2011.

Kim Cameron and Robert Quinn, *Diagnosing and Changing Organizational Culture - Based on the Competing Values Framework*, Jossey Bass, 2011.

John Kotter, *Leading Change*, Harvard Business Press, 1999.

Foster Provost and Tom Fawcett, *Data Science for Business - What you need to Know About Data Mining and Data-Analytic Thinking,* O'Reilly Media, 2013.

Harvard Business Review - multiple authors, *On Strategy*, Harvard Business School Publishing Corporation, 2011.

Marcella Bremer, *Organizational Culture Change - Unleash Your Organization's Potential in Circles of 10*, Kikker Groep, 2012.

Vodafone Group, *Vodafone IoT Barometer,* 2016. www.vodafone.com/iot

Numerex, *5 Key Ingredients for a Robust, End-to-End IoT Platform*, 2016. www.numerex.com

CFE Media, *2016 Digital Report - IIoT*, 2016. www.cfemedia.com

Gartner Research, *Five Business Ecosystem Strategies Drive Digital Innovation*, January 12, 2016. www.iotnow.com

Verizon, *State of the Market: Internet of Things 2016 - Accelerating Innovation, Productivity and Value*, www.verizon.com

Calleam Consulting Ltd, *Why Projects Fail,* www.calleam.com

Resources

These are a few key books that influenced and informed the creation of The BEST System, the StratGraph tool, IoTaudit, and the IoT Business Transformation System.

Simon Sinek, *Start with Why*, Portfolio/Penguin, 2009.

Napoleon Hill, *Think and Grow Rich*, Random House Publishing Group, 1937.

Chris McChesney, Sean Covey and Jim Huling, *The 4 Disciplines of Execution*, Free Press, 2012.

IoT Consulting and Support

In order to facilitate your IoT journey, there are several ways to supplement your IoT efforts:

IoT Consulting - http://enviro-controls.com/iot-consulting/ - The Enviro-Controls team provides consulting services for the IoT Business Transformation System.

IoTaudit - www.iotaudit.com - for a complete overview of the IoTaudit System tools including several hours of free instructional videos.

IoT Smart Overlay Platform as a Service - http://enviro-controls.com/iot-smart-overlay - explains the IoT Smart Overlay Paas in great detail including everything explained in this book.